THE

Royal Ocean Racing Club

MANUAL OF

WEATHER
AT SEA

THE
Royal Ocean Racing Club
MANUAL OF

WEATHER
AT SEA

DAG PIKE

David & Charles

Acknowledgments

My sincere thanks to all those who have let me loose with the weather on various record attempts and who have had to suffer from my weather decisions. My thanks also to various meteorological authorities who have been a tremendous help, particularly the staff at the Central Forecasting Office at Bracknell. Many people have helped me with advice and education during the reasearch for this book and I would like to thank them as well.

During the production of this book my assistant Gina Haines helped in a thousand ways, particularly with typing the manuscript and working on the index. Jess Bennett was a great help with the drawings and numerous people helped with the photos and other information. My grateful thanks to them all.

A DAVID & CHARLES BOOK

The Royal Ocean Racing Club

The Royal Ocean Racing Club was formed by the participants of the first Fastnet Race held in 1925. After the race the entrants formed the Ocean Racing Club, later to become the Royal Ocean Racing Club. Since 1925, the Fastnet and other races in the English Channel, North Sea, Irish Sea, (and also in the Mediterranean and the Far East) have been run on a regular basis, interrupted only by the Second World War.

The Fastnet is held biannually (there have been 34 Fastnet Races since 1925), and forms part of the Champagne Mumm Admiral's Cup series, first held as a team event to challenge the United States of America in 1957.

In addition to organising races and events, the RORC co-ordinates British participation in team events such as the Southern Cross, Sardinia Cup and IOR 'Ton Cup' world championships.

A handicap rule known as the RORC Rule was devised in 1925, giving each yacht a time allowance based on rating; this was the forerunner of the International Offshore Rule (IOR). Through the rating office, the RORC is the national authority for measurement and rating of offshore racing yachts, and administers the IOR and International Measurement System (IMS) in the UK.

Jointly with its French counterpart UNCL, the RORC devised and supervises worldwide the increasingly popular Tesco Channel Handicap System (CHS). RORC races cater for all three rating rules.

In 1990 the RORC was invited by the organisers of the Whitbread Round the World Race to oversee the development and administration of the new Whitbread Rule.

The RORC is not a governmental agency but is a private members club organising offshore racing for members and non-members alike and is closely involved in the development and management of yacht racing as a worldwide sport. Club membership is strictly limited to competent offshore yachtsmen and yachtswomen who qualify by completing a minimum mileage of offshore racing. There are currently 3,450 members.

The RORC has taken a keen interest in ensuring that yachts taking part in the races it organises are adequately equipped for the task, and has produced a comprehensive list of safety items that must be carried. Yachts that do not meet the RORC safety standards are not eligible to enter any of the RORC organised races.

Dag Pike

Dag Pike is a seaman by profession. Now well established as a marine journalist and author, Dag built his first boat at the age of twelve and went to sea as an apprentice in the Merchant Navy at the age of sixteen, going round the world three times. Qualifying as a ship's officer in 1954, Dag was employed on ships servicing lighthouses and buoys around the English coastline. After ten years, in which time he rose to captain, he left to become an Inspector of Lifeboats with the Royal National Lifeboat Institution. It was experience gained in this position, testing new designs of lifeboat and developing the world's first rigid inflatables, that led Dag in to writing.

His first book, *Powerboats in Rough Seas*, which is based largely on personal experience, was the definitive book on advanced powerboat handling. He has since written a sequel *Fast Boats and Rough Seas* which looks at the subject in greater depth. In all, Dag has written twenty books including: *Motor Sailing*; *Electronic Navigation for Small Craft*; *Fishing Boats and their Equipment*; *Electronics Afloat*; *Practical Motor Cruising*; *Boat Electrical Systems*; and *Fast Boat Navigation*.

Dag started offshore powerboat racing in 1969, competing in the first Round Britain Powerboat Race. Now a top navigator in this demanding sport, Dag has navigated for the World Champion Carlo Bonomi and in 1984 was navigator aboard the winning boat in the Round Britain Race. In 1988 he was navigator for Fabio Buzzi, winning the World Championships. He was selected as navigator on both the Virgin Atlantic Challenger transatlantic record attempts and as navigator and project director for the Italian Azimut Atlantic Challenger Trans Atlantic record attempts. In 1990 Dag was navigator aboard the boat which won eight out of the nine legs in the Venice to Monte Carlo Race, and in 1992 he was navigator on the successful attempt at the London–Monte Carlo record. Other recent successes include being skipper/navigator aboard *Drambuie Tantalus* on its successful Round Britain record attempt, and weather consultant to the Italian *Destriero* on their record-breaking Atlantic crossing.

His successes include being runner-up in the 1989 Yachtsman of the Year Award. He currently writes for yachting and shipping magazines in many parts of the world, works as a marine surveyor and consultant and is a Fellow of the Royal Institute for Navigation.

Weather has been an essential part of Dag's sea-going experience. On all the Atlantic and other record attempts Dag has been the 'Weatherman' making the decision when to leave and how to negotiate with the weather. 'Weather is an essential part of navigation particularly in fast boats and when you are riding in the boat you have to suffer if you make the wrong decision'.

Dag is in the weather 'hot seat' again in 1994 when he is navigator and weatherman on a Pacific record attempt.

Contents

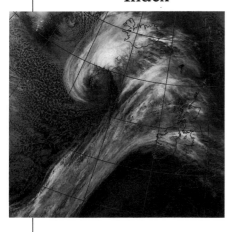

Extensive depression approaching British Isles

1 Four Dimensions

For the sailor the weather governs everything he does: it creates the risk in the form of rough seas, it creates the pleasure in the form of good sailing breezes or calm seas, it creates the pain in terms of rain and fog. Every move the sailor makes will depend in some way on the weather. An understanding of the weather and the way in which it affects the surface of the sea is thus an essential ingredient to yachting, increasing the pleasure and reducing the risks.

The weather conditions are just as important whether you are under sail or power. The requirements may be different, but it is the weather which dictates your speed, your pleasure and your pain. Under sail you may relish the fresh breeze which speeds you to your destination. Under power you will welcome the calm seas which allow you to use the performance potential of your boat to its maximum.

In harbour you will be more aware of the sun or rain aspects of the weather. At sea it is the wind and the waves it generates which are the important factors and which dictate your progress under power or sail. Visibility, or the lack of it, can also be very important and at sea you tend to become much more conscious of the changes in the weather and their impact than you do on land. On land we have come to terms with the weather to a considerable degree and the advance of civilisation has led to the provision of shelter from the rain and protection from the cold. Whether you become exposed to the effects of the weather on land is largely a matter of choice.

Keeping the Weather at Bay
At sea the element of choice is largely removed. Of course you can have a boat with a wheelhouse which will offer a degree of protection from the elements. Even in a sailboat you can get a measure of protection, but this is purely personal protection and it can't remove the fact that every inch of progress made by the boat is directly affected by the weather. The weather affects the movement of the boat and the level of comfort. There is no escape: it affects everything you do at sea.

Even at sea man has tried to isolate himself from the effects of the weather. The ocean liners are the prime example of the way in which size has been used to isolate passengers from the effects of sea and swell, to create an environment in which the weather would have the smallest possible impact on civilised society. It was successful up to a point, but in strong winds and rough seas it was always the weather which had the upper hand, dictating the progress and upsetting the carefully prepared timetables of man.

In a yacht you certainly don't have the luxury of size to reduce the impact of weather. You need to adopt a more conciliatory role, one where you have to negotiate with the weather even though it is from a position of weakness. Fighting against the weather is only likely to bring you pain and suffering; but understanding, negotiating and working with the weather should enable you to get along quite well most of the time.

Weather Forecasts

You are going to get along a lot better with the weather if you know what is going on. It is easy to assume that the weather forecasts will tell you all you want to know, but forecasts tend to give only the broad details of what the weather is going to do. Listen to any weather forecaster and you will hear the strong note of confidence in their voice, a voice which suggests that the weather pattern is firmly under control. Most of the time they will have a good grasp of what is going on, but if you then start to analyse some of the words the forecaster is using, you may begin to realise that there is an element of doubt. You will start to be aware that there can be a vagueness in the forecast which may reduce your faith in its quality.

When forecasters start to use the phrases 'I think' and 'probably', you can sense that this type of weather forecast is less than precise. Even shipping forecasts which can appear to be a model of precision can produce the same element of vagueness. What does the forecast mean when it says 'wind increasing later'? Is 'later' in 12 hours' time, or 24 hours' time? The difference could be critical to making a safe passage, so how can you get the sort of precise forecast which you need?

An understanding of the weather will help, but here it can be difficult to grasp just what we mean by weather. Of course we can picture what the forecaster means when he says it is going to rain. We know what he means when he says the wind will be blowing Force 5 from the SW. However, the forecast is just a little cameo of the weather, a picture of what the weather may be like in 12 hours' time given in terms of wind strength, rain, fog or other known features.

Weather Charts

You may get a weather chart by fax or other means and this can give you a better picture of the weather pattern. However, this weather chart is just a simulation of what the atmospheric pressure and the weather fronts might be at a particular moment. It is a static picture in two dimensions and far removed from the reality of the weather, the elements of which are constantly changing and interacting.

Television pictures showing the satellite view of cloud formations speeded up in time, so that you can get a visual picture of weather patterns, will help to give a better understanding of the flow of the weather, but they still tell only part of the story. They do not show the winds or sea conditions, the temperature or pressure, all of which are vital to a better understanding of what is going on.

There are more advanced weather charts which show the wind direction and strength. These are helpful to get a picture of what the weather is going to do, but again they show only the forecast winds at a frozen moment in time and only in general terms. Of course you are interested in these general weather pictures, but you are much more interested in the specific weather for the time and place you plan to go sailing.

The Fourth Dimension

Weather reports and weather forecasts are an extremely valuable aid to safe navigation, but they can be much more valuable when they are used to form a four dimensional picture of the weather. Most weather is presented as a two or perhaps three dimensional picture and it is important to grasp the concept that the weather is four dimensional. There is a vital vertical component to the weather which can have a significant outcome on future weather developments and give you a much better understanding of what is happening – but perhaps even more important to the sailor is the fourth dimension of time.

With advances in computer graphics it may be possible in the future to get a three dimensional picture of the weather with the vertical component included; but that will still be only part of the story. Such a picture will help you to build a better picture of the way the weather patterns are moving and interrelating; but each weather chart is still only a frozen moment in time. The element of time, the fourth dimension, can be included by looking at consecutive charts, though these tend to be at 12 or 24 hour intervals which can leave you with a lot of guesswork in between. Equally it is important to remember that any forecast, any picture or chart of the weather in the future can talk only in general terms.

The Limitations of Forecasts

If you listen to land weather forecasts these tend to be divided up into regions, each of which can cover quite large areas. The shipping forecasts are much the same with some of the forecast areas being quite extensive. Any forecast for areas or regions has to be an average of the conditions. If there are significant differences in the forecast for different parts of the region it will normally be divided up, but you don't have the luxury of this sort of help if you happen to be on or close to the borderline between two areas. In this situation *you* have to do the averaging, taking something from both forecasts and trying to come up with the best solution. The situation can be worse if you are at the intersection of four forecast areas.

So most of the forecasts can be only a general guide to what the weather will be. You then have to make allowances for the effect of local conditions. For instance high cliffs or a range of hills could significantly

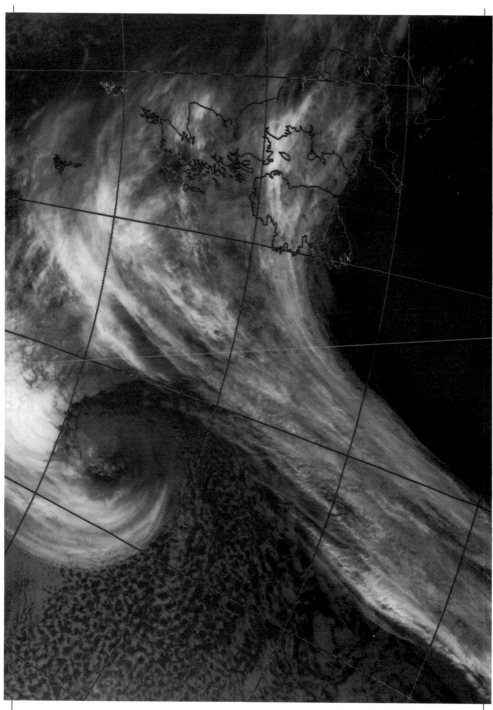

A satellite photo showing an extensive depression approaching the British Isles. Satellite pictures like this can show the forecasters exactly what is happening and it is possible to receive similar but less sharp images at sea direct from the satellites.

FOUR DIMENSIONS

affect the weather locally. You may hear people suggest that an area has its own 'local' weather which doesn't relate accurately to the weather forecasts. Such 'local' weather can often be the result of geographical features.

You may well have to make allowances for 'local' weather conditions in coastal waters. Wind strengths can increase around headlands and you may also find wind shifts in these areas. These are 'local' weather phenomena which you will never find spelt out in weather forecasts, yet they can have a significant influence on the conditions in which you are sailing.

At the end of the day, the feature which is probably of most interest to you, the sea condition, is not even mentioned in most forecasts. This is mainly because sea conditions also change on a local basis and can be directly affected by time-variable factors such as tides and sea breezes. The local effects of these on sea conditions can be even more variable than those of the wind.

The Forecaster and You

The forecasters do a good job and this book is not meant to be a criticism of what they do. They have to match up a lot of different requirements in their forecasts. Most yachtsmen will happily accept what the forecaster says as gospel and lay their plans accordingly. This brings bitter recriminations when the forecast doesn't work out as planned, particularly when the wind is lighter or stronger than forecast. It can be galling to have a forecast of strong winds and cancel a day's sailing only to find that the strong winds do not arrive until the evening. Once again the forecaster gets the blame – and the weather forecaster is rather like the football goalkeeper, they get remembered for the ones they got wrong and not the ones they got right.

We are now provided with so much weather information and it is generally presented in such a positive way that we no longer question its validity or, more importantly, make our own assessment of it. You listen to the forecast and take what the forecaster says for granted without questioning it. If you listen carefully to what the forecaster is saying you can become aware of a certain vagueness creeping into the forecast, a degree of uncertainty, which may mean that the forecast is not perhaps as reliable as it seems. So often the forecast can appear vague particularly when it comes to timing, and this is partly the result of each forecast covering a large area. When a change in the weather occurs in one part of that area, it may take some time to reach other parts of the same area. Later in this book we will look at some of the language which forecasters use and what they mean by apparently vague terms.

Sometimes this apparent vagueness is hard to correlate with the image of weather forecasting as an exact science. Meteorological Offices (or, as they are usually called, Met Offices) are quick to point out the powerful computers which they employ to generate weather maps, the skilled and experienced forecasters they employ to interpret these weather maps and

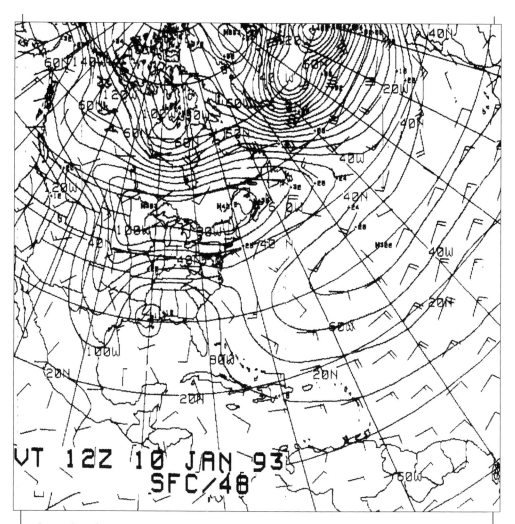

A weather chart as received by a dedicated weatherfax receiver. This chart covers most of the Atlantic as well as the north polar regions and requires careful study to extract the required weather information

the quality of the information they provide to the public. The days of interrogating wet seaweed and looking for significant signs in the sky may be long gone, and weather forecasts may have assumed a quality of information hardly credible thirty years ago, but there is still an enormous gap to overcome in translating this high quality information to meet the individual requirements of each user.

The problem faced by the weather forecasters is one of trying to be all things to all men. One forecast may have to meet the needs of a vast number of people with widely differing requirements for weather information. The family sitting on the beach will be concerned about the sun and the temperature. When a local sea breeze springs up in the afternoon they will blame the weather forecaster because he didn't mention in the countrywide weather forecast that it would be cooler on that beach on that afternoon.

Even the dedicated marine forecasts still leave a lot to be desired in providing the right sort of information for sailors. A marine forecast will certainly give wind direction and speed, but this will relate to open sea conditions. The forecast is far too broad in nature to mention local variations in terms of both the timing of change and the effect of local topography. Few marine forecasts will mention sea conditions because the size and type of waves can vary on a very local basis when tides and topography are taken into account. That sea breeze which led the family on the beach to complain about its effect on the temperature could also lead to a sailor complaining because he thought the calm conditions forecast would be ideal for anchoring off the same beach.

Fee or Free?

There is an enormous amount of weather information available, much of it free, and some higher quality information available on payment. There is a reluctance on the part of Met Offices to release longer term weather forecasts and specialised local forecasts on a free access basis and you usually have to pay for them. As Met Offices tend to become more commercial in their outlook, this trend is likely to continue so that access to personalised weather forecasts will be limited to those prepared to pay. At the same time there is a reluctance amongst yacht skippers to pay for weather information when so much apparently good quality information is available for free.

There has to be a meeting point between these two apparently conflicting attitudes and it can be found by a careful analysis of the weather information which is available without charge. If the yachtsman takes the trouble to analyse the forecasts in more detail and to match this with an understanding of the weather, how it is formed, and how it affects the sea, then there is no reason why the quality of the weather forecast information cannot be raised to that available from a professional forecaster without having to pay for the privilege.

Developing a Feel for the Weather

To take this step towards a better quality of weather forecast does require getting involved with the weather. Forecasts tend to present the weather as something which develops step by step in time with the forecast periods. It tends to be presented as very much a two dimensional feature just related to the surface of the earth or sea. In reality the weather is a constantly changing and evolving system. The weather develops in a four dimensional process and to grasp the fundamentals of the process and have a reasonable understanding of the weather, then you need to have some emotion, some feel for the weather.

If you have this emotional feel for the weather then you will be able to see the various processes taking place as weather patterns evolve. As a yachtsman you will not have time for the intense study of the weather necessary to unravel much of the weather 'mystique', but these days the very powerful computers which are used to analyse the weather and produce forecast charts do much of the hard work. Aided by experienced meteorologists who fine-tune the weather charts, the basic information about the weather and its future pattern of behaviour is readily available. What you as a yachtsman need to do is to translate this raw material into specific information relevant to your needs.

There is no need to go to the trouble of producing your own forecasts from scratch. You could never hope to equal what the computers and forecasters do within an extensive worldwide weather organisation. What you can do is take their material, and it is widely and readily available, and build on this to personalise the information. There is no magic formula for this, no secret information which the experts cannot see: it is a simple matter of looking at the weather patterns and changes from a very personal perspective. In this way you can work out what the weather will be and what changes will occur along the personal route that you are following or propose to follow in your yacht.

You don't need any special equipment for this process other than a measure of common sense and a willingness to try to understand, even empathise with the weather. The analysis of the weather can be carried out in the comfort of your own home or at a chart table on board. You will need access to weather charts and a barometer is helpful, but you will need to spend far less on the equipment for weather charts than you would on electronic navigation. We tend to spend a lot of money on electronics for navigation to reduce the risks of running aground and to be able to find our way to harbour, but there does seem to be a reluctance to spend money on equipment to upgrade the quality of the weather information we receive. Yet the risks from the weather can be as great, if not greater than those from faulty navigation.

Be Weatherwise

In time it is possible that computer programs will be able to take over some of the weather analysis methods proposed in this book. Already weather charts can be obtained through programs on personal computers when the latter are linked to a radio receiver. In the future the same programs may be able to carry out some of the more detailed analysis required to personalise the weather information. In the meantime, the manual methods proposed here are relatively easy and straightforward and well within the capabilities of any competent yacht sailor.

Before weather forecasts became readily available and seafarers had to rely on their own judgement formed by assessing the weather signs which were visible to them, they were constantly aware of every subtle change in the weather. Their lives would often depend on their own analysis of the weather. Today because of the ready availability of weather forecasts we have become lazy about the weather. The careful analysis is apparently being done for us, so why look any further? The problem is that we

FOUR DIMENSIONS

assume that the weather analysis is being done for *us*. In reality it is a very coarse analysis which is being done for thousands of others at the same time. To get the personal approach, to really know what the weather is doing in your particular part of the world you need to get involved, to take the weather analysis on from where the forecaster leaves off and to add the valuable dimension of time, which is the key to good weather planning. We tend to be told of the changes which are going to occur but if we can add an accurate time to when the forecast changes will occur in our locality then we will have a real understanding of the weather and will know not only what is going on but when.

This book starts with a look at where you can get weather information and forecasts, and these are covered in more detail in the back of the book. These are the building blocks for weather analysis together with an understanding of the way in which different types of weather are formed. With this background, forecasts can be analysed in a practical way which will lead not only to a higher quality of weather forecasts but also to an interest, an excitement and a feeling about the weather. It was Benjamin Franklin who said, 'Some are weatherwise, some are otherwise'. Hopefully this book will put you in the first category and give you a better understanding, an instinct for, even an emotional involvement in, the environment of yachting.

2 Weather Information

There is such a wealth of weather information available to sailors that there really is no excuse for not knowing what is going on in the weather world in general terms. Weather charts, weather forecasts, weather reports available on paper, by radio, by television and by special request as well as the possibility of obtaining personal weather forecasts all add up to a vast amount of weather information which can be used to find out and understand what is going on as far as weather is concerned. The first step towards understanding the weather involves getting weather information from as many sources as possible. This is what we will look at in this chapter, but it has to be remembered that the weather reports and forecasts are only part of the battle. The next stage, which we will look at later on, is how to interpret these forecasts, what validity can be put upon the forecasts, and how to use them to best advantage to make your sailing as safe, secure and pleasant as possible.

Four Kinds of Forecast
The reports and forecasts can be divided into four main groups. The first of these and probably the most significant as far as yachtsmen are concerned is the dedicated marine forecast which reports conditions and gives forecasts for coastal and ocean water areas. Because they are so obviously maritime these forecasts are of particular significance to the yacht sailor and should form the main basis for decision making. Marine forecasts are generally broadcast by radio on the basis that this is a common medium available to all at sea or planning to go to sea. Some newspapers and some TV stations will also produce marine forecasts and these can be in the form of weather maps as well as written or verbal forecasts. These marine forecasts will give the forecast wind strength and direction, a measure of the visibility and some indication of the general weather. Some may include an indication of the sea conditions and there can also be a basic description of the general weather pattern.

These marine forecasts can be backed up and, if possible, correlated with the forecasts for land areas. These are widely available in newspapers, on the radio and on TV. Such forecasts are obviously valuable, but tend to place less emphasis on the wind and more on the cloud and rain conditions and temperatures. The weather doesn't generally make a sudden change from the land to the sea, and so these land forecasts can provide useful information about the weather in coastal waters, but the main difference to be noted is that wind strengths tend to be given as light or moderate rather than in Beaufort wind scale numbers. Wind direction may be less precise than yachtsmen would like, but you have to appreciate that the wind is much more variable over the land and so it is less easy for the forecaster to be precise. There is a much stronger emphasis on temperature and rain in these land forecasts than on other weather factors such as visibility conditions which can be of primary interest to yachts.

The third type of forecast available is what might be termed the 'meteorological weather reports'. These tend to come in the form of charts showing the general isobar patterns which either exist or are forecast for a particular area. Some of these charts, particularly those found in newspapers, show the general weather patterns such as the highs and lows and the fronts as well as an indication of what the associated weather will be. Such charts do not require much interpretation but they will often lack the detail required for a valid analysis of the weather. They are a development from the basic weather charts issued by meteorological offices which tend to show the isobars and fronts only. These basic charts are the main building blocks of weather forecasting and they have to be

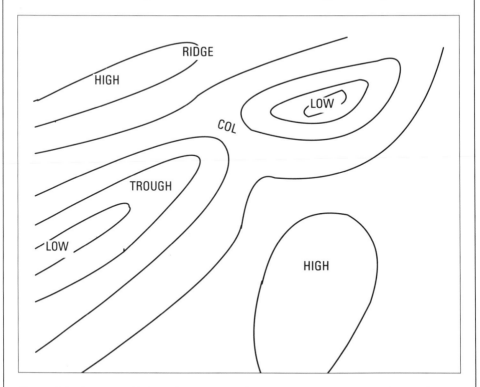

Some of the features which are found on weather maps. In many respects the weather map looks like the height contours on a land map but it should be remembered that the lines link places with equal barometric pressure.

interpreted in order to deduce what the resulting weather might be. It is charts like these which form the basis of all weather forecasting, and therefore most of the basic information which you need to assess future weather conditions is contained in these charts. For the weather-educated sailor, these charts can be particularly valuable. They come in a variety of forms, some showing the sea level isobars, others showing water temperatures and conditions in the upper layers of the atmosphere.

The fourth source of weather information is satellite pictures. Looking at the weather from the other side has provided forecasters with a valuable new tool and TV has taken advantage of this to show the moving sequence of weather patterns. This has certainly helped to improve our visualisation of the weather in four dimensions and in addition to seeing these pictures on TV it is also possible to receive them directly on a computer connected to suitable radio receivers.

Receiving Forecasts

When you are in harbour it is possible to get access to all these different sources of weather information although you do have to get organised or have specific equipment for some of them. With modern communications it is also possible to get the weather information from most of these sources whilst you are at sea, although some items such as television reports may not be so easy to receive at sea unless you are close to land or have special receiving antennae. Weather maps, and even satellite weather pictures can be obtained at sea these days via weatherfax equipment and this should be the aim of every sailor who really wants to know what is going on in terms of the weather. Weatherfax receivers are a comparatively expensive piece of equipment for a yacht but against this investment has to be weighed the value of the weather information they provide.

A modern alternative to the weatherfax is to connect a suitable SSB radio receiver to a computer and with the right software you have free availability to all the weatherfax charts. Provided that you already have the computer – which can be a normal 286 or higher PC or laptop – then this can be a cheaper alternative to a dedicated weatherfax receiver. The computer can be used for a variety of other purposes such as displaying electronic charts and receiving telex messages. The laptop type of computer is better than the desk-top PC because it has lower electrical power requirements and is better suited to a yacht environment.

Even a simple broadcast radio receiver can be a useful source of weather information and should be considered to be the minimum requirement on board for receiving weather information. Such a receiver will pick up most land and marine forecasts. A communications receiver working on either VHF or HF will give access to specialised marine forecasts which are sent from radio stations or coastguards. In many cases these will give similar information to the marine forecasts given over broadcast radio frequencies but HF radio can also give access to ocean weather forecasts. The SSB radio used for connecting to a computer for receiving weatherfax will also be able to pick up these ocean weather

WEATHER INFORMATION

broadcasts, and some of the software programs associated with the computer weatherfax systems can translate those weather forecasts sent out in Morse code into plain language.

These computer based systems can also give the yachtsman access to Navtex broadcasts. These broadcasts cover both weather and safety information and have the advantage that the received message is automatically received and printed out without any action being required on the part of the recipient. Dedicated Navtex receivers are also available for this purpose.

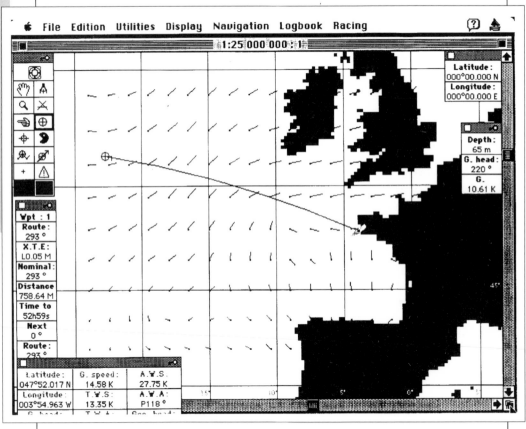

A computer print out of wind information from the Macsea program which provides combined weather and navigation information.

Everything Has Its Price

At the end of the day, as far as weather information is concerned, you tend to get what you pay for, so that the better the quality of equipment you have on board for getting weather information, in general the better the quality of the information you will receive. Because of the ready availability of free weather information from sources which rely simply on existing communications equipment on board, there does tend to be a reluctance amongst yachtsmen to invest in some of the dedicated equipment such as weatherfax and Navtex receivers or the combined computer based systems. However, without this equipment and the weather charts and other information it brings, you will have to rely on other people's assessment and interpretation of the weather patterns rather than on your own. This may work quite satisfactorily much of the time, but you will be aware only of part of the story of what is going on in respect of the weather. You will not be able to build up that emotion and feel for developing weather situations which is essential to a deeper understanding. It is not a very satisfactory situation either when you are trying to fine-tune the weather forecast to your own particular requirements. Once you appreciate that the weather dominates and influences virtually everything you do at sea, then the more you know about the weather and what is going on, the more comfortable you can be that you will be able to work with the weather or even negotiate with the weather to use it to the best advantage.

Land Area Forecasts
Land area forecasts are broadcast by most radio stations around the world, and are obviously aimed at the general public and its requirements for weather information. These forecasts vary in character a great deal, some being very vague and others giving a very precise indication of future weather conditions. The vague ones are likely to say something such as, 'Today will be bright and sunny with a small chance of showers', which is fine if you are thinking of going down to the beach, but doesn't help much if you are a sailor who is concerned about what the sea conditions might be like outside the harbour. Forecasts of this type will often cover a large area, for instance you can get forecasts like this included in most news bulletins, but they might have to cover the whole of the British Isles in just two or three sentences which means that they are very general.

Most radio stations will have certain times dedicated to more specific weather forecasts, but even then just two or three minutes does not give a lot of time to cover the weather pattern and forecasts, particularly if the radio station covers quite an extensive area. In these days when we are seeing more and more local radio stations, then there is a better chance of getting more specific forecasts applicable to local areas, and these can be a valuable source of weather information particularly where the local radio station is based on the coast when it will often include a forecast for the coastal sea areas.

Land area forecasts will tend to focus on the possibility of rain, and there will be a strong emphasis on expected temperatures. Whilst winds tend to be mentioned there is a degree of vagueness about the strength, partly because wind strength can vary considerably over land areas, depending to a certain extent on the terrain, and therefore it is not easy to be particularly precise about forecast wind strengths. For coastal land radio stations where there is an attempt to indicate the marine conditions you will also find a degree of vagueness, in most cases with seas being described as moderate or rough rather than specific wave heights being given. This can be partly due to the fact that sea conditions can vary considerably even in closely adjacent coastal waters, because of tidal streams and exposed headlands, and the forecaster is generally not too explicit about conditions because of these variations.

Most land forecasts tend to be made in the morning and the evening. These are the times when people tend to need weather information, with the morning forecasts concentrating on the weather for the rest of that particular day and perhaps into the evening, whilst the evening forecast will tend to concentrate on the weather for the following day. The maximum period for land forecasts is generally 24 hours but often there will be a further outlook included in the forecasts which can extend up to 48 hours ahead. Certainly these land forecasts can be useful for getting a general impression of the weather conditions. Remembering that yachting is mainly designed for pleasure, they will let you know whether there is going to be sunshine and the sort of temperatures you can expect, items which can often be missing from the marine forecasts, and so they can be a great help in deciding whether you are going to anchor off the beach and enjoy a swim. For serious safety weather information, land forecasts probably leave a lot to be desired, but that doesn't mean that you should ignore them, and they can be a useful source of local weather information when some of the marine forecasts cover much more extensive areas.

In the USA there are specific radio stations, dedicated to providing 24 hour weather information, which tend to follow a regular pattern with repeats and updates every hour or so. Such weather stations can be a very valuable source of information, though with this type of information you have to be very careful to sort out the difference between weather reports and weather forecasts. With the time available to these continuous weather stations it is often possible to get much more specific weather reports and forecasts for local areas which can be very valuable for your planning purposes, but like most of the land forecasts it is not always easy to build up the general pattern of the weather in relation to highs, lows and frontal systems, which is the sort of information that you need to build up that picture in your mind of what the weather is doing and how it is going to develop.

Marine Radio Forecasts
For most yachtsmen marine forecasts are the primary source of information. Most developed countries around the world put out marine broadcasts for shipping and for small craft, and whilst the format and content may vary, the basic concept is still much the same. The intention is to give the sailor an idea of what the general weather pattern is, followed by more detailed forecasts for particular sea areas combined with actual weather reports from stations in many of those sea areas. Taken at face value it would seem that forecasts of this type should provide you with all the information that you might need to make your plans and develop your tactics on a cruise as far as the weather is concerned. Sadly the reality is

somewhat different, and whilst these marine radio forecasts have great value, they do not tell the complete story.

There are various reasons for this inadequacy, but one of the major ones is the inevitable limit to what can be put across to the listener in such a comparatively short period of time to give them an indication of what the weather patterns are doing. At best you can only build up a broad picture of what the weather is doing from the information given out in marine forecasts, always assuming that these forecasts include a section giving the general weather situation. Because it is the way that depressions and frontal systems move which dictates or determines most of the changes in the weather, this general picture of the weather situation can be of vital interest to the navigator. Without this more detailed description of the general weather situation the navigator is really left with having to take the forecast at face value, or do quite a lot of work in trying to develop his own weather chart from the information given.

A good marine forecast should provide enough information for the

Pressure and pressure tendency	
Steady	Change less than 0.1 mb in 3 hours
Rising slowly or falling slowly	Change 0.1 to 1.5 mb in last 3 hours
Rising or falling	Change 1.6 to 3.5 mb in last 3 hours
Rising quickly or falling quickly	Change 3.6 to 6.0 mb in last 3 hours
Rising or falling very rapidly	Change of more than 6.0 mb in last 3 hours
Now falling, now rising	Change from rising to falling or vice versa within last 3 hours

The terms used to describe pressure tendency in the coastal station reports.

navigator to be able to draw up their own weather chart in broad terms. There is often enough information given to do this but the work involved is not always the sort of thing you want to do at sea and it requires considerable confidence in your ability to be sure that you have got it right if you intend to base your tactics on the map you have drawn up. Of course if this is the best weather information you have, then you will have to make do with it. It looks easy and simple drawing up the weather map and there are special charts to help get the information down in the correct way from the forecast – and in harbour you could probably cope. In the confines of a small yacht tossing about at sea, it not only becomes a lot more difficult but it may not always be possible to spare the time to do this type of work, particularly if you are sailing short-handed.

This leaves you with having to accept the actual forecast as your prime means of information from these radio broadcasts, and here you have to remember that the forecast is based on weather information which has been collated and assessed several hours previously, and in most cases the forecast is only for 24 hours ahead. These can be significant limitations when you are trying to plan a strategy because there may be a change in the weather occurring just outside the forecast period which you might have been aware of from the analysis of the general weather pattern but which is not timed to show up within the 24 hour forecast. If you are planning a voyage over exposed waters covering, say, 48 hours, then this lack of advanced information could have serious consequences.

Marine radio forecasts can come from a wide variety of different sources. In many countries they are broadcast by entertainment radio stations at prescribed times, and the British pattern of broadcast marine forecasts is a good example. Here the shipping forecasts which are sent out four times a day are supplemented by inshore water forecasts by local radio stations which are usually put out in the morning and evening, which will give you weather information to plan for the current day and the following day. Many of these local radio marine forecasts are quite specific and deal with comparatively local conditions, something which the more general shipping forecasts cannot hope to do because of the large areas which are involved.

Overseas Marine Forecasts
Supplementing these transmissions from broadcasting stations there are weather forecasts broadcast by the coastguard organisation in most countries. These are broadcast on both VHF and HF marine band frequencies and in general are very similar to those produced by the marine forecasts put out over broadcast frequencies. In the USA the dedicated weather channels on radio include marine forecasts, some of which are general covering considerable sea areas and others which are very localised and cover both reports of current conditions and forecasts of future conditions, usually for a period of 24 hours ahead.

It is fine when these broadcasts are in English. This makes them comparatively easy to understand, always assuming that you know what the terminology means as used in the forecasts. This does vary from country to country and in Britain what might be called 'moderate seas' could translate into American as a 'moderate chop', but we will look at this terminology later on when we talk about how to interpret weather forecasts. If you sail into the waters of continental Europe, then you may well get weather forecasts broadcast in English from coast radio stations and sometimes from local coastguard stations, but in general they will tend to use their native language. Although it may sound daunting to translate this weather forecast into English, it is not as difficult as it seems and it only means understanding some of the key words associated with the weather in order to get an adequate picture of what is going on. A short vocabulary showing some of these words is given in the Appendix at the back of this book, and this should be enough to translate a weather forecast, particularly after you have had two or three goes at it and start to understand the format in which the forecast is presented and the way in which the terminology is used.

One of the biggest difficulties in understanding foreign language broadcasts is in determining the sea areas which are referred to in the broadcast. The sea areas used by the British Met Office are also used by other countries bordering the North Sea and a map of these sea areas is included overleaf.

Another factor which is important in any forecast is to know the time of the forecast. There is obviously a delay between the preparation of a forecast and the time it is broadcast and if you are going to compare different forecasts or try and assess when changes will occur in your area then you need to know the time that the forecast originated. This is usually given in the forecast but may not be easy to understand in foreign language broadcasts.

In general then, it is possible to get plenty of marine weather information in almost any waters in which you are sailing, but you do need to make preparations in order to receive this. If you are planning a voyage then part of the planning should include a list of the various radio stations which broadcast weather information, the frequency on which they operate, and most important of all, the times at which the broadcasts are made. It is not always easy to find this information readily at hand, although most nautical almanacs are a good source of such information. The Admiralty List of Radio Signals Volume 3 is also a mine of information about where weather information can be obtained and it lists every radio station around the world which makes weather broadcasts. The frequencies on which broadcasts are made do change from time to time so you will need an up-to-date copy of the book, but if you are serious about the weather then this Admiralty book is a vital piece of equipment. The book itself is quite complex so analysing your requirements and listing the various transmitting stations will help you to receive the required information at the right time.

The main requirement for receiving marine broadcasts will be receivers operating on marine band VHF or HF. Broadcasts on VHF frequencies tend to be more local in nature because of the shorter range of this radio equipment. Most yachts have a VHF radio on board these days but you can get more information if you supplement this with a simple broadcast receiver. If your budget runs to it, a more sophisticated receiver which can receive single sideband transmissions on the HF frequencies will be even better and this can form the basis of a computer based system for receiving fax and Navtex weather information.

Newspapers
There is a great tendency to dismiss the forecast given by newspapers on the basis that they are invariably out of date. Certainly any forecast which appears in a newspaper is probably going to be twelve hours old by the time you read it, and you will probably get much more up-to-date information from radio broadcasts – but don't dismiss it because of this.

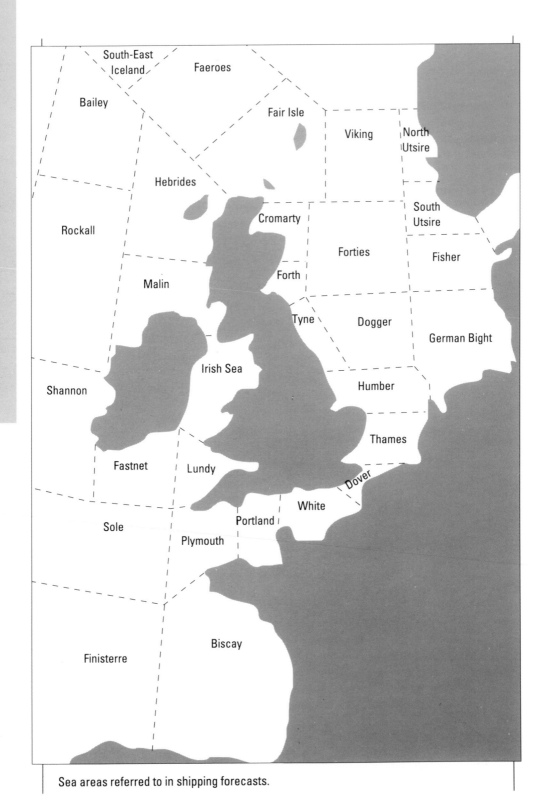

Sea areas referred to in shipping forecasts.

The most important aspect of the newspaper forecast is the weather chart which is often printed alongside the written forecast. This weather chart immediately gives you that vital mental picture of the weather patterns and the general weather situation which can be difficult to assess from a radio broadcast. From this you can start to put the other elements of the weather forecast into place and start to understand what is happening. It is from this picture of the weather that you can then start to translate the more general weather forecasts as broadcast over the radio into more specific forecasts to meet your particular requirements. One of the most critical aspects of any weather forecast is the timing of change. In most broadcast weather forecasts any timing is likely to be particularly vague, simply because the forecast tends to cover such wide areas, and obviously the time it takes for a change to pass through a particular area can vary considerably from one side of the area to the other. The forecaster tends to make his assessment or forecast in rather vague terms as far as timing goes. If you have the weather map in front of you, even though it may be twelve hours old, and you have this vital mental picture of the weather, then suddenly the weather situation can come alive, and you can get a much better idea of when changes in the weather pattern are likely to occur in the particular area in which you find yourself. The weather map will also help you to assess changes in the local weather which are occurring whilst you are at sea, so that you can relate these to the general weather pattern and the expected changes.

Of course you can't get newspapers at sea and so these newspaper weather charts are only of value at the planning stage. Some of them also tend to be a bit vague in the way they are drawn, the artist aiming to produce a colourful image of the weather, rather than an accurate picture of the isobars and frontal systems. If you are planning to use these newspaper forecasts then choose your newspaper carefully in order to get the best quality of weather map and one which has at least a time alongside it so that you have a basis from which to work. Ideally the chart should have the isobars at 4 mb intervals rather than the 8 mb intervals normally used. With 8 mb intervals many of the more detailed weather features which are of great interest will not be clearly visible.

Television Forecasts
Television has opened up a whole new way of presenting weather information and it has become something of an art form. The way in which weather information is presented on television will vary from country to country and of course you are at a disadvantage if you don't understand the language, but most forecasts are presented on television graphically, so that even if you don't know the language you can still get a fairly clear picture of what is going on. Probably the most valuable aspect of the television forecast is the weather maps which are used as part of the presentation. These full colour weather maps generally show isobars and frontal systems as well as lows and highs, and these can not only be shown for a particular time but with modern computer graphics they can

be moved forward on a time basis so that you can get a very clear idea of the way the weather patterns are changing and developing. These are what might be termed three dimensional weather maps, as opposed to the two dimensional ones which are issued on paper which only show the weather at one specific time. This ability to show the weather patterns changing with time is a significant aid when you are trying to build up a mental picture of the changing situation.

The problem with TV broadcasts is that they tend to be very limited in time and so you only get a brief glimpse of these sequential weather maps almost as though the presenter is conjuring up the weather with a magic wand. There is certainly never enough time to study the maps in any sort of detail and relate them to where you are or where you are going to be so that you can see how the weather situation will change at that particular place. One way out of this dilemma is to record the weather forecast on video tape and have a video machine which allows either slow play-back or even a freeze frame so that you can then study the weather map at your leisure and allow the sequences to move on only after you have analysed what is going on in your particular location or in the area in which you are interested at the time of that forecast chart. You will have to live with the fact that the weather presenter is standing in front of the chart and may be blocking your view of the part of the chart in which you are interested.

These TV presentations are developing into some of the most interesting and exciting weather information which is obtainable because it takes the weather maps into the dimension of time. Whilst the graphics used on the TV weather charts may not suit the purist meteorologists because the isobars are often not quantified and the weather maps often cover a very large area, at least this type of information is a considerable step towards a clearer understanding of the weather. On TV presentations the weather charts are often combined with sequential charts showing the cloud cover as taken by photograph from satellites – though again the sequences are run too quickly to get a full appreciation of what is going on. If you can record them on video cassette and study them at your leisure, you are obviously going to get much more valuable weather information than is possible from almost any other source and you should have a very good basis on which to make your judgement of weather.

When watching TV weather charts and presentations you have to be aware that these tend to be developed primarily for land based viewers. The charts will show wind strengths and directions, but these tend to be only in very general terms with perhaps five or six wind arrows covering the wind pattern over the whole of the British Isles. The same goes for the weather information which tends to be fairly generalised, and although many TV stations will give out more specific regional forecasts, the area which a particular TV station covers is generally large enough to rule out specific weather information for local areas. There are exceptions of course and in some countries you may get more specific TV weather forecasts, particularly where large cities are located along the coast but like the radio forecasts, these more specific local forecasts still cannot take into account local sea and wind conditions which can occur because of the tides or the topography of the coastline. For instance no forecast of this type is going to show the tidal race which might occur off a headland, and in order to anticipate this you have to start putting your own interpretation on to the forecast, in order to gauge the local conditions.

Telephone Information

When it comes to getting information about the weather there is nothing quite like the ability to be able to talk directly to a forecaster. The forecaster will have made his assessment of the prevailing and forecast conditions and if you can tell him where you plan to be at what particular time, he will be able to tell you fairly precisely just what weather conditions you can expect. Unfortunately weather forecasters cost money and advice of this type is rarely free. It is generally available only if you have made previous arrangements to call into the forecast office and have paid the necessary fee for doing so. Most services relating to weather which are available via the telephone do cost money, but as we said earlier the quality of weather information does tend to improve the more you are prepared to pay for it and this type of paid weather information is available in most countries.

In Britain there are a number of weather centres around the country where this facility is available and in order to make maximum use of any phone calls of this type relating to weather information it is advisable to have a copy of a current weather map in front of you because then you will be able to appreciate much more clearly what the weather forecaster is trying to indicate. It also helps to have a general knowledge of the weather and the way fronts and depressions are formed and behave, because not only will the forecaster appreciate talking to someone who has weather knowledge, so that they don't have to spell out every small detail of the weather situation, but you will also get a much better appreciation of what the forecaster is trying to tell you. The value of this type of forecast information is that they can be very, very precise in terms of details specific to your requirements. The interesting aspect of this personalised type of detailed weather information which the forecaster is giving you is that it is the sort of information you could work out for yourself if you were to take the trouble to get the right sort of basic weather forecast information and learn how to interpret it.

Commercial Forecasts

Most of the weather forecasting authorities are national organisations, with the Meteorological Office in Britain being a good example. However there is a growing number of private weather forecasting companies being set up in order to provide specific types of weather information for specific requirements. Once again you have to pay for these services because they are commercial operations, but it is possible to get very precise and specific weather information from these sources. An example of this is

Noble Denton which operates a forecast centre in central London. This is open 24 hours a day and they receive meteorological data from a variety of sources around the world. Experienced forecasters analyse this and come up with specific forecasts to meet your requirements. These can be sent out by telephone or fax, or you can talk directly to the forecaster to discuss your requirements and what he thinks is going to happen. Companies like Noble Denton will also supply regular forecasts for three days ahead and even a further outlook beyond this period, but as we said before, this type of service does cost money and generally has to be arranged in advance.

More general weather information can be obtained through special telephone lines. In Britain there are two of these, one called Marine Call which deals specifically with marine forecasts, and the other Weather Call, which deals with land forecasts. By dialling a specific number you will get a recorded message which can either cover a specific area or can give you a three to five day general outlook for all coastal areas. An extension of this Marine Call service is the Marine Call Club where you pay an introductory fee which is currently £10 and then you can prepay for your calls for the service which are available at a discount rate. The forecasts produced by these phone systems will be general rather than specific to your particular requirements.

Weather Reports
Whilst you are primarily interested in forecasts rather than weather reports, it can be useful to get weather reports direct from coastal stations before you set out, so that you have some idea of the actual conditions prevailing. Most coastguard stations will accept telephone calls enquiring about the current weather conditions. The trend is to have fewer of these manned stations and you should remember that some of the modern coastguard stations are not based on the coast itself because they tend to work through radio communications rather than via a lookout system. Any weather report gained from a coastguard station or other station along the coast needs to be treated with a degree of caution because coastguard stations are often located high up on cliffs, often on a headland where the wind strength could be considerably more than might be found at sea level. If you are going to use weather reports from this source as a means of assessing what the weather conditions are like outside before you set sail, then remember that they do not always indicate what is happening at sea level and they represent a very local assessment of the prevailing weather conditions.

There is no doubt that there is a lot of information available on the end of a telephone, though increasingly yachtsmen are being expected to pay for weather information obtained in this way, whether it comes from the Met Office or from private sources. Telephone weather information can be valuable particularly as a guide to making your plans before you go to sea. Similar information can be obtained at sea via a link through VHF or if you are reasonably close inshore using a mobile phone, but this does tend to put up the cost. While weather information obtained over the telephone

Wind force at sea when coastal winds are onshore	Factor by which to multiply coastal station wind to obtain wind over the sea	
	By day	By night
4	1.1	1.7
5	1.3	1.6
6	1.4	1.8
7	1.3	1.6
8	1.3	1.6
9	no figures	1.6

The wind will always tend to be less over land than at sea and these tables give the factors by which to multiply wind strength as given in the reports from coastal stations. They are increased at night because wind strengths tend to be underestimated on land at night.

When using this table bear in mind that a high land station could experience a stronger wind than that at sea level and that the wind can be accelerated around headlands.

Wind force at sea when coastal station wind is routed over land	Factor by which to multiply coastal station wind to obtain wind over the sea	
	By day	By night
5	1.2	1.6
6	1.4	1.9
7	1.6	1.6
8	1.7	1.8
9	no figures	1.8

is certainly a valuable addition to the repertoire available to the sailor it is possible to get a very similar quality of information supplied free provided that you have the required receiving equipment on board.

Navtex and Weatherfax
These two methods of obtaining weather information have been put together here because they both require dedicated equipment. However they do have the advantage that once you have invested in the equipment, the information supplied is free of charge and the operation of the equipment is to a certain degree largely automatic. In these two respects these two systems of obtaining weather information are probably the best available on the market today, although their value has still not been widely appreciated by yachtsmen.

Navtex
A Navtex receiver is rather like a small telex unit which operates in the receive-only mode. It is tuned to a preset frequency, that on which the Navtex transmissions are made and the messages received are printed out

on a paper printer which is an integral part of the equipment. Left to its own devices a Navtex receiver will print out information from all the transmitting stations within the area of reception, but most receivers can be made selective, so that they receive information only from selected transmitters or of selected types.

In addition to weather forecasts and gale warnings, Navtex receivers will also print out navigation warnings and distress messages. The distress messages cannot be filtered out but the remainder can, although of course both navigation warnings and weather information are important to safe navigation and the only filtering likely to be done by a yachtsman with a Navtex receiver is to be selective in the stations from which the information is received. This narrows down the information to the waters in which the yacht is sailing.

The big bonus with a Navtex receiver is that the weather forecast and gale warnings are written down for you. There is no need to tune in and wait for specific radio broadcasts and so you never miss a weather forecast as can happen with verbal messages. Each transmitting station covering an area will transmit the forecast for the next 24 hours for the sea areas both in and adjacent to that region, and in addition you get a general synopsis, so you have enough weather information for your immediate requirements – but you do not have the full weather information as given on some shipping forecasts which enables you to build up a complete weather map from the information given.

Navtex is part of the Global Marine Distress and Safety System (GMDSS). GMDSS is a worldwide system which ensures that vessels at sea which are fitted with specified communications equipment can receive and transmit distress messages at all times and can also receive weather information and other safety messages. GMDSS comprises a variety of basic equipment such as satellite communication systems, HF and MF radios and VHF radios and other communication systems such as Navtex. Whilst much of this equipment will be outside the range of that fitted to yachts, Navtex is certainly worthwhile considering as a source of weather information, and because it works on the 518 KHZ frequency the range of the transmissions is quite extensive, up to 300 miles or so. For yachts fitted with VHF radio only it provides a useful source of weather information if they go outside the range of the VHF transmissions.

Weatherfax

Like Navtex, weatherfax receivers also print out the weather information, but they do this in the form of weather charts rather than as printed words. Apart from the difference in format of weatherfax, there is a considerable similarity between this system and Navtex – except, too, that weatherfax operates on high frequencies and so is available on a worldwide basis and can provide a wide range of weather information.

Weatherfax is available from transmitting stations around the world and whilst each transmitting station has a similar type of output comprising weather maps showing the current weather situation and forecast weather patterns for up to five days ahead as well as wind, sea and swell charts, and even upper atmosphere pressure charts, the format of the various charts and what they contain will vary to a certain degree with the various transmitting stations. The area covered by the weather charts will also vary from station to station so that USA weatherfax transmitters will generally produce information covering the Pacific, the Atlantic and the Caribbean regions, whilst European stations will cover the Atlantic and Mediterranean areas, and so forth.

Schedules of the frequencies on which stations worldwide transmit are contained in the Admiralty List of Radio Signals Volume 3, and similar official publications. These schedules cover the transmission times for the various weather maps which are available and the various frequencies on which the transmissions are made. Different frequencies in the high frequency band are required and these are selected dependent to a large degree on the range of the yacht from the transmitting stations and the time of day. The frequencies vary in this way because of different propagation characteristics of the atmosphere and in general the longer the range from the transmitter, the higher the frequency required. Many modern weatherfax receivers will automatically sample the various transmissions on the different frequencies and select the best frequency for reception without any action on the part of the operator. This means that all that is necessary to receive weather maps is to select the station from which transmissions are required, and to a large extent the weatherfax receiver will do the rest.

When you are out at sea weatherfax is the best method available of receiving the actual weather charts and of course the system will work just as well in harbour. The system already described for receiving weatherfax charts, using an SSB radio linked to a computer, is a viable alternative and should produce good quality charts. Failing any of this specialised equipment you can plot your own charts manually from information provided from shipping forecasts, but the accuracy and quality will be only at a barely acceptable level. The full scale weatherfax charts are vital in order to get a full and up-to-the-minute picture of what the weather is doing, and the fact that you can get sequential charts for every 24 hours for the next three or five days means that you can have a full appreciation of how the weather patterns are changing. This enables you to make strategic decisions in respect of the anticipated weather and can help with weather routeing on longer voyages, something that is not always easy to do when you are working with just 24 hour forecasts.

Weatherfax also has a value before you leave port because if you get the weather charts two or three days before you sail, then you have a much better appreciation of the whole weather situation, which helps you to interpret the radio weather forecasts more effectively. With weatherfax you have to appreciate that what you are receiving is not so much a weather forecast as a forecast chart of the isobars so that you can see where highs,

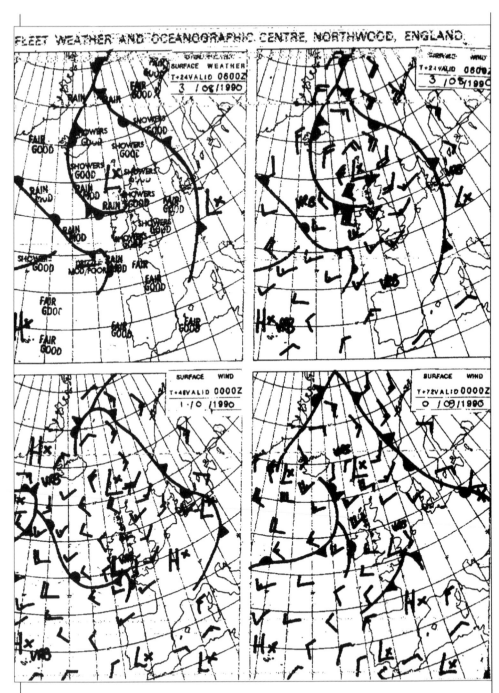

A very useful weatherfax page of information showing, clockwise from top left:

1 The general weather conditions and fronts for 24 hours ahead
2 The winds and fronts for 24 hours ahead
3 The winds and fronts for 72 hours ahead
4 The winds and fronts for 48 hours ahead

lows and frontal systems are located. This raw weather information needs to be interpreted in order to make an assessment of what the weather is likely to be, and to a certain extent this is what the radio forecasts will do for you; but with a reasonable understanding of the weather and how it is formed you should be able to make your own assessment of the anticipated weather from these charts and have a much better 'feel' for what the weather is doing, so that you are not faced with any nasty surprises.

Some of this interpretation of the raw weather charts is done on the weatherfax and comes in the form of forecast wind, sea and swell charts. The wind charts can be particularly valuable for a sailing boat, but you have to appreciate that they come in very general terms with the chart normally covering a large sea area such as the whole of the eastern Atlantic. Such a chart will show the general trends of the wind patterns and strengths, but obviously cannot show the sort of detail changes which are specific to your area of interest. Much the same applies to the sea and swell charts which are only applicable to open sea areas anyway and cannot take into account changes in sea and swell conditions generated by tides or other local conditions. So these weather charts available over the weatherfax are very important items in your weather forecasting repertoire, but they will not tell the whole story and have to be used alongside other sources of weather information, one of the most important of which we will look at next.

Visual Weather Observations

It is very easy to get hooked into what weather forecasts say and take it as gospel, whilst ignoring what is actually going on around you. Visual observation of the weather was the only information available to sailors at one time but even with the wealth of other information available today these visual observations still have a role to play. Obviously you will be aware of what the wind and sea conditions are because these are directly related to the performance of your yacht and the comfort and pleasure of the voyage, but there is a whole host of other weather information which can be gleaned from visual observations. If used intelligently this information can enable you to fine-tune weather forecasts. These visual observations will help you to anticipate to a much closer degree changes in wind strength and direction, and if you relate them also to the coastal geography and the tidal conditions, then you will be able to anticipate improvement or worsening in the sea conditions.

In the days before weather forecasts became commonplace and we started to place reliance in these forecasts, mariners had little else except visual observations of what was going on around them to anticipate what the weather might do. Many of the old weather sayings are based on specific observations of weather changes and many of these contain a great deal of truth in them, but they tended to apply to local areas rather than being a blanket means of anticipating change.

Weather features such as frontal systems have reasonably distinctive and reliable sequences of cloud changes which indicate not only the type of frontal system which may be approaching, but also your position within the frontal system. As frontal systems represent one of the major features which herald changes in the weather patterns this can be valuable information. The use of the barometer can also show changes in the weather patterns, and here you are more interested in the change of the barometer readings rather than the actual reading itself. Many yachtsmen today will faithfully record the observed weather patterns in the log book, showing the wind direction and strength, the barometer readings and the temperature. There is a feeling that these are recorded for posterity rather than for any practical reason and yet this is the way in which the general weather forecast obtained by radio or weatherfax can be fine-tuned to your particular location and situation.

Bringing It All Together
From the foregoing you will realise that there is an enormous amount of weather information available to the yachtsman. We will look at how to analyse this later on in the book but what you need to consider is how to be selective in order to get what you need to give you a reasonable picture of the weather and what it will be doing at least in the next 24 hours and perhaps even further ahead. With so much information available, you could spend a great deal of your time at sea just on weather forecasts. Because you have to attend to the navigation and the actual sailing of the yacht, your time for obtaining forecasts is limited, so you need to be selective in the weather information which you decide to use, partly to make sure that you have adequate information, but also to ensure that collecting weather information doesn't become a full time job. You will also need to know where to invest money in the right equipment because you don't want to overload the yacht and its electrical systems with equipment which is duplicating other sources of information.

The point has already been made how weather charts are vital to building up that all important picture of the weather situation, both now and in the future. Weather charts are available from a weatherfax, from a computer system and from newspapers and television, and you can make up your own charts from the information given in shipping forecasts. Obviously the weatherfax is the primary source of weather charts, and if you are really concerned about getting quality weather information, then a weatherfax receiver should be at the top of your list of priorities. A weatherfax combined with receiving shipping forecasts over the radio, and visual observations will give you all the information about the weather which you are likely to want. Unfortunately the electrical systems on many yachts cannot support the requirements of a weatherfax and the budget of the owner may not be able to run to the investment in a weatherfax. However, owners coming into this category tend to operate in coastal waters with reasonably frequent stops in harbour, so the weather maps taken from newspapers or from television could provide an acceptable substitute, provided they can be obtained on a regular basis.

As far as broadcast weather forecasts are concerned, a Navtex receiver probably provides the best solution because of its automatic operation and the fact that you don't need to tune in at a specific time to listen to the weather forecast. An acceptable substitute and one which will be cheaper and more versatile is to have a radio receiver with built-in tape recorder, which allows you to record the broadcast and then play it back at your leisure, rather than the hurried rush to scribble it all down. It is possible to get radio receivers with a timing device incorporated, so that they automatically switch on and record the weather forecast at preset times, and this can be particularly valuable for those forecasts which occur in the middle of the night when you may be fast asleep.

You might supplement the specific shipping forecasts or marine forecasts with information from local radio stations which can give information more specific to the particular area in which you are operating, but there is a need for caution if you get weather information from too many diverse sources because you may find it conflicting, which can confuse rather than clarify the weather situation. The reason for any conflict is usually because of a difference in timing. Forecasts from different sources can be based on information collated and analysed at different times, and information from different sources can present a confusing picture if you are not fully aware of the timing at which analysis has been made and to which predictions relate.

For a coastal passage, radio weather forecasts combined with access to a weather map are probably more than adequate for requirements, but for a longer passage at sea involving two days or more when a weatherfax is not available on board, then investing in the cost of a discussion with a weather forecaster about the trends and developments in the weather pattern could be a very valuable investment. Weather forecasts today are remarkably accurate, particularly in general terms about the behaviour of weather patterns. They are developed using computer models which run on some of the world's most powerful computers and form a reliable basis for future action. The weather forecaster will be able to give you a picture for at least two or three days ahead with a high degree of reliability, and if you then relate this to your visual observations of the changes of the weather and the developing situation, then you will be able to fine-tune this general forecast to the specific conditions in which you find yourself and will be able to anticipate when and how changes in wind and sea conditions are likely to occur. It is best to make any arrangements for this type of personal weather forecast before you leave harbour.

Reading Between the Lines

It is very easy to take a weather forecast at face value and accept that that is how things are going to be. Modern forecasting is a reasonably exact science thanks to the extensive use of computers and their capabilities of generating an overall picture of the way in which weather patterns are going to change for up to five days or more ahead. It is easy to think that such computer forecasts, combined with the analytical skill of the human forecaster, are all that might be required to provide adequate weather information. But the fact that the weather forecaster needs continually to analyse and review the weather information is indicative that weather forecasting is still some way from being a precise science, and you have to appreciate that weather forecasts have to be given in general, rather than precise terms. It is for this reason that obtaining weather forecasts is only a partial solution to knowing what is going on. What you have to do as a yachtsman and a seaman is interpret these weather forecasts, firstly to understand the language which is used in the forecasts or the meaning of the lines and symbols in the weather maps, and then to relate these to the specific observations that you make in your location and the influence that land features and tides can have on the weather. In this way you will have a much better understanding of the whole weather situation and will be much more confident in using this as a basis for future decisions.

In the next chapter we go on to look at this question of interpreting the weather forecast, and how that can give us some idea of the meaning, emotion and even drama which lie behind the stark words and pictures contained in those forecasts.

3 Weather Forecasts

Y ou might well ask why there is any need to interpret weather forecasts when a forecast apparently gives you all the information you need. Any good marine forecast will give you the wind strength and direction and usually some idea of the visibility and perhaps even the sea conditions which can be expected. On the face of it that is all you need to make an assessment of whether the conditions are suitable for planning a voyage or deciding on tactic. However, if you look at the forecasts closely you will realise that they ask almost as many questions as they answer.

One of the first factors to consider in any forecast is that of timing. If you are going to draw any reasonable conclusions from the forecast then the timing element, the fourth dimension, is very important. Weather forecasts tend to be rather like a two dimensional map and indeed this is what the weather maps are, and it is only by looking at successive weather maps that you can get an idea of the fourth dimension which is time. Once you introduce the element of time into a forecast, then you can see how the weather patterns are moving both in terms of speed and direction and from this you will be able to get a much better appreciation of just when changes in the weather will reach your particular locality. It is in this matter of time that most weather forecasts become somewhat vague, and yet to you the yachtsman, timing of any weather change can be vitally important. It is only when you know the time of change that you can then decide whether you have adequate time to complete the particular passage you are planning before the change occurs, or whether the bad weather indicated by the change may overtake you before you reach the safety of harbour. This matter of timing can also decide whether you should seek shelter or even whether you should leave harbour in the first place. If you can pin down the timing of a weather change accurately, this can be of particular value in a fast powerboat where passages may be no longer than two or three hours in length and it is often possible to take advantage of a short lull in the weather. You may be able to complete a passage before the bad weather reaches your locality or if you know that deteriorating weather is coming along you can change your plans and run away from it provided that you know when the weather changes are going to occur.

When Was the Forecast Made?

In order to pin down this timing aspect more accurately, the first thing to establish is the timing of the actual forecast. Some forecasts may be started by the message, 'Here is the weather forecast for the next 24 hours'. With this message you know that the forecast is for 24 hours from the time of broadcast. However you have to bear in mind that the forecast has been put together with information which was obtained earlier. Most weather forecasts these days are based on computer developed weather maps, and the computers generate these every 12 hours, normally at midnight and midday. In order to ensure compatibility with the various computer models for the weather which are run throughout the world, Greenwich Mean Time or – as it is known in the weather world – Zulu, is used as the standard time, and so these computer runs are timed for midnight and midday GMT, or – as you will see marked on weather charts – for 0000Z or 1200Z.

The information which is fed into the computer in order to generate these weather maps comes from weather observations from a wide variety of sources, ships at sea, land stations, observation balloons, satellite pictures etc, and all of this information is usually obtained in a period of up to 6 hours prior to the computer run. It is easy to see that there could be a delay of 12 hours or more between the actual observations of the weather and the forecast information reaching you via the radio. Such a delay is inevitable, and there is not much you can do about it even with the best quality information. There is no reason to suppose that the weather information given to you is any the less accurate because of this delay. What you have to establish is the actual time when the forecast was made by the weather forecaster, and that could vary between 3 and 12 hours before you actually receive the forecast, the actual delay depending very much on the type of information and the way it is transmitted.

When is Later?

The reason for having to establish this time is that any relative timings used in the forecast may be based on the time at which the forecast was first transmitted, rather than the time at which it is received. The same forecast can be received at different times depending on whether it is sent by broadcast radio, as a coastguard message or by Navtex. So when the forecaster starts to use terms like 'later' or 'imminent', you have to know what time these relate to. Marine forecasts tend to work for 24 hour periods and in these situations the word 'imminent' is generally used when a weather change is going to occur within 6 hours of the issue of the forecast – which means that by the time you receive the forecast the change could already be occurring. The word 'soon' generally means between 6 and 12 hours from the time of issue, and the word 'later' generally means anything beyond 12 hours and up to the 24 hour period of the forecast. The delay in transmission could mean that although the forecast is for a 24 hour period, you are actually into that period by the time you receive the forecast.

With land forecasts, the forecast changes tend to relate more to the time of day, so the forecaster will tend to use the words 'morning', 'afternoon' or 'evening' rather than 'imminent', 'soon' or 'later'. The time span involved might be much the same but it is important to understand what the forecaster is talking about when he talks about time.

You will notice in this discussion on time, that the phrases used to denote time in forecasts are comparatively vague. Nothing is much more precise than a period of 6 hours yet a boat, particularly a powerboat, can cover a large distance in that time, so a more precise timing would be extremely valuable. The reason for the vagueness as regards time is not difficult to see when you look at the comparatively large areas which are often covered when the forecasting area is divided up into regions. The forecast area for marine purposes could cover a sea area 100–200 miles in extent and in open ocean areas this could extend up to 500 miles. Obviously if a weather pattern is moving it will influence one end of this area before the other. If you take the frontal system which could denote a significant weather change and which might travel at a speed of twenty knots, it could take ten hours to traverse a particular sea area creating considerably different weather conditions at one end of the sea area from that of the other during its passage. Despite this, the forecaster has to try and average things out and condense this change into a few words, and from this you can quickly begin to realise the difficulty in being any more precise with the timing. This is where you have to play your part in interpreting the weather forecasts, because you know exactly the location where you want the forecast to apply, whereas the weather forecaster when he generates his forecast is talking about the weather over sea areas extending to many hundreds of square miles.

The problems of timing can be magnified if you find yourself on the border line between two sea areas, or worse still at the junction point of four sea areas. Now the forecast area which is of interest to you is extended considerably and in order to arrive at a reasonable idea of what may be going on you have to try and put together the forecasts for the different areas involved and try and make an assessment of what will happen in your particular locality at a particular time.

Progress of Fronts

In order to do this, you really need to have a weather map in front of you, and this is where the weatherfax can be particularly valuable. If you have one or preferably two sequential weather maps covering a 24 hour period, then you can get a picture of how the weather patterns are moving, particularly low pressure areas and frontal systems, and from this you should be able to get a much better impression of when changes in the weather relating to the passage of a frontal system will occur. Depressions can move at speeds of up to sixty knots although more usually they are moving at speeds of twenty to forty knots. Associated frontal systems tend to move a bit slower, generally between ten and forty knots, but if you have two consecutive weather maps then it is comparatively easy to work out the speed of advance of each feature.

What will be of particular interest to you will be the relative locations of the frontal systems over a 24 hour period. If you transfer the positions of the centre of low pressure areas and the frontal systems from a chart 24 hours ahead on to a current chart, then you will quickly be able to see the relative positions and movements of these systems. From this it is a comparatively simple matter to interpolate between the two lines marking the positions of a front to work out either the position of the front at a particular time, or probably more importantly the time at which that particular frontal system will cross your current position. We shall go into the actual changes of weather which can be expected with the passage of frontal systems in later chapters but if you bear in mind that these frontal systems tend to be responsible for the major changes in wind direction and strength, with wind changes up to 120 degrees being possible in a comparatively short period of time during the passage of a front, then you need to know the timing of this occurrence in your locality.

Speed of Pressure Systems	
Slowly	up to 15 knots
Steadily	15 to 25 knots
Rather quickly	25 to 35 knots
Rapidly	35 to 45 knots
Very rapidly	over 45 knots

Terms used in forecasts to describe the speed of movement of pressure systems.

The wind strength given in the forecast will still be relevant, but by relating the forecast to the weather chart in this way you will be able to give a much more precise time for the increases or decreases in wind strength given in the forecast, and more importantly you will have personalised these for your own particular requirements. It is by using methods similar to these that a professional weather forecaster is able to give you a very accurate forecast in terms of both timing and conditions for a particular locality at a particular time. Such is the accuracy of forecasting these days that he can give a very positive opinion in most cases about the sort of conditions which can be expected at a particular time and place. The forecaster's skills are based largely on extensive experience, but you have one advantage over the forecaster in that you can also make visual observations of the actual conditions prevailing at your location, and from these observations it is also possible to get a more precise indication of the changes which are occurring. These changes – which particularly relate to cloud formations – can indicate the particular part of a frontal system which you are encountering. This in turn enables the location of that front to be pinpointed with considerable accuracy and in this way you can actually chart the progress of the weather front which has been shown on the forecast chart, or has been mentioned in the general situation part of the weather forecast. You should bear in mind that when a front is marked on a weather map the position refers to the point where the actual change between warm and cold air occurs at sea level. The effects of the front can extend several hundred miles in front of this point at higher altitudes.

If you cannot get hold of two consecutive weather maps it is still possible to predict the speed of movement of frontal systems by the distance apart of the isobars. In general the closer together the isobars, the faster the front will be moving, and it is possible to get a scale which can be laid across the isobars to indicate the speed of the front. Even if you don't have such a scale you can assume that a vigorous depression will move at thirty knots, the associated warm front will move at fifteen knots and the cold front at twenty knots. These figures will enable you to plot the position of a front to estimate the time it will cross your position or you can know where it will be at a specific time. So now you have a much more precise update of the way the whole weather pattern is moving, and from that you will be able to fix with much more precision the timing of any future changes which are forecast.

Barometer and Thermometer Readings

It is not just visual observations which can help to pin down more exactly the timing information of the weather forecast but also readings of the barometer and thermometer. Changes of pressure and temperature occur with the passage of a frontal system and the changes in readings are more interesting than the actual levels of the readings themselves. If you log these readings at regular intervals, say every two hours, you can become aware of the changes which are occurring and in turn be more precise about the timing of future weather events. These changes in pressure and temperature become more important at night time, when it is far less easy to assess the changes in cloud cover and quality. On a particularly dark night the changes in the barometer readings may be your only indication of weather changes, so these log readings should not just be looked upon as something to look back on with memorable pleasure when you study previous cruises. They have an important role to play in providing immediate historical data about the weather and the relative changes taking place, and are one more source of information when you are trying to put together the global picture.

Winds Light to Variable

In the same way that you can upgrade the accuracy of the timing of changes which might be forecast for the weather, you can often upgrade the quality of the actual weather information itself. Once again forecasters are faced with this problem of producing an average forecast for quite a large sea area, and it is in trying to come up with a reasonable average that they tend to introduce a note of vagueness into the forecast. Unless weather patterns are particularly stable you will rarely find a marine forecast giving a precise wind strength on the Beaufort Scale. Even a

WEATHER FORECASTS

Beaufort Number	Mean Velocity in Knots	BEAUFORT WIND SCALE		Probable Heights of Waves in Metres
		Descriptive Term	Deep Sea Criterion	
0	‹1	Calm	Sea like a mirror.	
1	1-3	Light breeze	Ripples with the appearance of scales are formed but without foam crests.	0.1(0.1)
2	4-6	Light breeze	Small wavelets, still short but more pronounced. Crests have a glassy appearance.	0.2(0.3)
3	7-10	Gentle breeze	Large wavelets. Crests begin to break. Foam of glassy appearance. Perhaps scattered white horses.	0.6(1.0)
4	11-16	Mod. breeze	Small waves, becoming longer: fairly frequent horses.	1(1.5)
5	17-21	Fresh breeze	Moderate waves, taking a more pronounced long form; many white horses are formed. (Chance of some spray).	2(2.5)
6	22-27	Strong breeze	Large waves begin to form, the white foam crests are more extensive everywhere. (Probably some spray).	3(4.0)
7	28-33	Near gale	Sea heaps up and white foam from breaking waves begins to be blown in streaks along the direction of the wind.	4(5.5)
8	34-40	Gale	Moderately high waves of greater length; edges of crests begin to break in to spindrift. The foam is blown in well-marked streaks along the direction of the wind.	5.5 (7.5)
9	41-47	Strong gale	High waves. Dense streaks of foam along the direction of the wind. Crests of waves begin to topple, tumble and roll over. Spray may affect visibility.	7 (10.0)
10	48-55	Storm	Very high waves with long overhanging crests. The resulting foam in great patches is blown in dense white streaks along the direction of the wind. On the whole the surface of the sea takes a white appearance. The tumbling of the sea becomes heavy and shocklike. Visibility affected.	9 (12.5)
11	56-63	Violent storm	Exceptionally high waves. (Small and medium sized ships might be for a time lost to view behind the waves). The sea is completely covered with white long patches of foam lying along the direction of the wind. Everywhere the edges of the wave crests are blown into froth. Visibility affected.	11.5 (16)
12	64+	Hurricane	The air is filled with foam and spray. Sea completely white with driving spray; visibility very seriously affected.	14 (–)

precise figure on the Beaufort Scale still means a wind variance which can have a difference of five knots or more between the upper and lower speeds in that band of the Beaufort Scale. Much more likely is that the forecast will read something like 'Winds Force 3 to 4 and occasionally 5', and then you have a considerable note of vagueness coming into the forecast. For a small boat Force 3 or 4 might be a pleasant sailing breeze, but Force 5 could well mean it is time to take in a reef or it could produce the sort of conditions where you might not want to have small children on board. For a powerboat, a wind of Force 3 could allow comfortable progress at high speed. Force 5 could mean that you wish you had never left harbour and you have a rough ride which puts a strain on both boat and crew. In Force 3 the wind could be as little as seven knots. In Force 5 it could be as high as twenty-one knots.

Forecasters are probably being deliberately vague when producing such a forecast and you can't really blame them for this. They are trying to produce an average forecast over a considerably large area of sea and the conditions may be such that you could find a Force 3 over quite a large extent of that sea area, but there could be Force 5 in other parts. Forecasters would not be doing their job if they didn't warn of the possibility of Force 5 winds in the sea area, but on the other hand they don't want to be unduly pessimistic, and so the Force 3 or 4 is what they would generally anticipate to be the wind over most of the region.

There could be many reasons for the variation in anticipated wind speeds. On a showery day there will always be local increases of wind near areas where showers occur and these could be one reason for the different possible wind speeds. Another factor is that the wind gradient, which we will discuss later, may not be consistent over the whole of the sea area and therefore different wind strengths could be expected in different parts of the area, while land and sea breezes could account for considerable variations in wind strength near the coast. Another reason for variations in wind strength could be the funnelling effect of the wind around headlands and in estuaries, and the prudent mariner should always bear in mind these local variations in wind strength which can be anticipated but which tend to be too local in nature to be found in the general area forecasts.

Every Word Counts
Another point to bear in mind when it comes to looking at the wind strength factor as far as forecasts are concerned, is that you have to start understanding the language the forecasters use. This may appear to have a degree of vagueness about it, although the language forecasters use is actually quite precise. The words 'occasionally', 'locally', and 'temporarily', are often found in forecasts and really sound as though forecasters are hedging their bets when they use these words and are a bit uncertain about what is going to happen. To a certain extent this is true, but what it really means is that they are certain about the uncertainty. The word 'occasional' could be used to infer that the wind may increase in strength up one or two numbers on the Beaufort Scale from the general

average, and what the forecaster is saying when he uses the word 'occasionally' is that the situation is not particularly settled and that gusts or even more persistent winds may be found of higher speeds. This could relate to showery conditions, but it could equally mean that the isobars seen on the weather chart are not following nice regular curves but have a degree of waviness about them which could produce occasional increases in wind strength. The term 'locally' has a similar meaning, although generally it means that any variation from the norm will be comparatively local in extent whereas 'occasional' tends to relate to time rather than area. 'Temporarily' could refer to an increase in wind strength which occurs perhaps with the passage of a front when the wind could increase for an hour or two and then drop again. This is different from an occasional increase, because it is more precise and will almost certainly occur wherever you are in the region, whereas 'occasional' introduces an element of chance in much the same way as the word 'locally' does.

The forecaster has to use these words in the forecast, partly to make sure that the forecast user is aware of all the possibilities which might occur. Remember that forecasters have only a very limited time or space in which to get their message across, so you do need to listen to the forecast message very carefully and there is always a significance in each of the words the forecaster uses. The wording of a forecast can introduce an element of frustration for the listener, because what the forecast may be saying is that the wind may increase in strength quite considerably; and whilst you need to be warned of this, there is no guarantee that the wind increase *is* going to happen. This apparent indecisiveness can be very frustrating when you are trying to plan a day's sailing, and so often the weather forecast is on the border line between what may or may not constitute good weather for cruising. Taken at its average prospect, the weather forecast sounds quite reasonable, but taken at its worst possibility the conditions may be less than inviting. You have to remember that with any forecast situation, what the forecaster says is not gospel, and there is always the risk that conditions may deteriorate with stronger winds than forecast, or conversely the wind could die away and leave you without a good sailing breeze.

Localised Factors

When these conditions do occur the blame can usually be found in some local influence or disturbance. Sea breezes are a prime example and if the flow of the air generated by the sea breeze is close to the ambient wind direction, then you can find a considerable increase in wind strength perhaps by as much as ten or fifteen knots compared with the forecast wind. You can even get the wind strength changing when the tide changes because the moving water tends to drag the air along with it, although here the difference in speed will be comparatively small compared to that found with sea breezes.

Local effects such as this tend to be ignored in weather forecasts although you may well find them mentioned in local coastal forecasts where the effects are likely to be more pronounced and the forecast more local. Wind flowing over a peninsula can also be affected by its passage over the land, and so you could find very different wind conditions on either side of the peninsula even though the relative positions of the observations may be quite close.

There are so many possibilities with these local wind conditions that it can make the forecaster's job very difficult, particularly when it comes to coastal waters. One reason why the forecast areas out in the open ocean are much larger than those found inshore, is that out in the open ocean you tend to get much more consistent wind conditions and there are far fewer local variations compared with inshore waters.

Wind direction is generally of less concern than wind strength and in almost any conditions you must expect some variation in wind direction. The forecasters will tend to be reasonably precise if there is a good steady airflow across an extensive region, but generally they will give a wind direction as north westerly, rather than north west, and they will rarely be more precise than to give the wind direction at 45 degree intervals. For most practical purposes this is adequate and probably matches the degree of accuracy about which the forecaster can be confident, but it can introduce a degree of frustration perhaps in a powerboat where you are looking for the wind coming off the land only to find that it is running along the coast and you are faced with a head sea when you expected sheltered waters. You cannot always blame the forecaster for this situation because the wind which the forecast says will be from a direction somewhere just off the land may well end up running parallel to the coast through local diversionary effects. You need to be particularly cautious about this situation when you are trying to seek shelter from strong winds because what looks like a sheltered bay from a study of the chart and a knowledge of the forecast wind could sometimes end up as still exposed to the wind, where this wind is diverted from its regular pattern by coastal features.

Forecasting Wind Speed and Direction
When trying to analyse the forecast wind direction and speed, you can be reasonably confident in open waters that the forecasters have got their sums right. If you find the forecasters starting to introduce what appears to be an element of vagueness into the speed or direction then you can be reasonably confident that they are doing this because there is a degree of uncertainty about either or both of these factors, and that element of uncertainty should make you a bit more cautious in your approach.

Uncertainties in forecasting wind speed and direction can be appreciated when you look at the way in which wind strength and direction are calculated from the weather charts. Wind speed is found from measuring the distance between adjacent isobars in the region for which the forecast is required. When this distance is measured up against a special scale which will vary with latitude, then the anticipated wind speed for the time at which the chart was forecast can be estimated. Wind

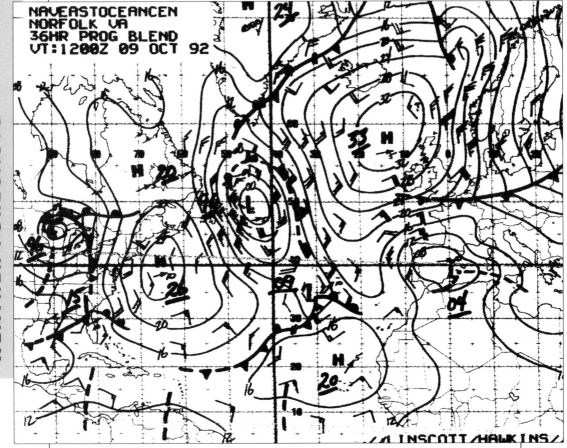

A weather chart of the North Atlantic which incorporates both wind arrows and isobars. Note the close affinity between the wind arrows and the direction of the isobars.

direction is normally gauged from the direction in which the isobars lie and is based largely on the knowledge that wind direction will to a large extent follow the lines of isobars, but will move inwards slightly towards the centre of a depression and outwards slightly from the isobar lines with a high pressure area.

This estimation of wind direction and speed will be looked at more closely in later chapters when we study high and low pressure areas, but the important thing to appreciate here when making forecasts from weather charts is that the weather chart itself is an approximation of where and how the isobars will lie for the prescribed time ahead. The lines drawn on the chart to represent the isobars represent the average direction and distance apart as forecast by the computer, and the lines generally are smoothed out and ignore possible small irregularities, which of course could produce local variations in wind strength and direction. Such irregularities are more likely to be found in areas close to land, where the heating of the land masses will be different from that of the sea areas so that these temperature differences can produce local variations in the wind. This is seen with land and sea breezes but there can also be local variations caused by frontal systems and thunderstorms, particularly when these are active areas of weather which tend to produce the stronger winds, meaning that there is probably a greater chance of local variations in wind strength and direction when the winds are strong, rather than in lighter conditions.

Forecasting wind strength and direction has become a skilled art as far as forecasters are concerned, and you should certainly never ignore what the forecaster suggests will be the wind strength and direction, but the point to remember is that the forecaster is producing the general forecast whereas you are much more interested in specific forecasts for the area where you are or where you intend to be at the time of the forecast. This is where you can bring a new meaning to forecasting by fine-tuning the meteorologists' general forecast into a specific forecast for your requirements, and in this way you can hope to take some of the surprises out of local weather conditions and plan your cruises with a greater degree of certainty.

Forecasting Sea Conditions
Wind speed and direction are comparatively easy to forecast, but the sea conditions relating to these wind conditions are much more difficult to anticipate from the forecaster's point of view except in open ocean areas. The forecast charts for sea and swell conditions are generally restricted to open sea areas only. It is possible to get forecasts of the sea conditions for more enclosed sea areas such as the North Sea or the English Channel, but even here forecasters are only producing their forecast of the average sea conditions and not the specific sea conditions which might be found in local areas. It is the specific sea conditions which will particularly interest you as a yachtsman, and for this you will have to make your own forecast because the conditions are going to vary with time and with locality, even over comparatively small distances of ten miles or less.

This question of forecasting sea conditions is a complex one and to a large degree has to be based on experience. The sea conditions will vary with both wind and tide conditions and the interaction between the two, but also with the proximity to land, the depth of the water and even the shape of headlands. It is possible to forecast the conditions in a specific area with a considerable degree of accuracy, but because sea conditions can vary tremendously even over a very small area of sea and with time, this is an area where you need to do your own forecasting rather than rely on what the weather forecaster has to offer. Out in the open sea, say over 100 miles from land, then the forecast charts of wave and swell conditions can be remarkably accurate and reliable. These wave and swell charts are available for up to five days ahead, and are generated by computer modelling which has been fine-tuned from experience, and the result is charts which can give a good indication of the basic conditions which can be expected. Once again with these forecast charts you have to do your own interpretation to get a better indication of what exactly the conditions might be in your locality.

Wave Height

As far as the wave height forecasts are concerned, these are based on average wave heights in average conditions and relate directly to the wind strength and fetch, which is the distance to windward from the nearest land. The figure usually given for wave height is the significant wave height, which is defined as the average height of those waves which are in the top one-third in a particular wave pattern. Even in a steady wave train, waves vary enormously in height, with some being two or three times the average height. By using the average height of the highest third of waves, the forecasters will hope to take out any nasty surprises from the wave patterns as forecast, but you have to remember that lurking within that significant wave height there will always be waves which could be considerably higher than the forecast average. Just as you can find strong gusts of wind perhaps up to Force 9 in a forecast wind of Force 6 or 7, so you could find waves up to two metres high when the forecast suggests that the average wave height will be only one metre.

As a prudent mariner you have to be aware of these eventualities, and even the larger waves are not likely to create much of a problem unless you are running very close to the limits of what a particular boat can take at the time when a larger wave approaches. If you keep something in reserve, which is the prudent way to operate, then these larger waves should not create any problem, just as gusts of wind can normally be taken in your stride. When you are interpreting the forecasts you have to keep in mind that a forecast wave height does not mean consistent waves of that particular height but average waves of that height.

It is the same with forecast swell conditions, and here again swell heights will vary. Swell conditions are unlikely to affect the average yacht sailing in ocean conditions, but these swell forecasts do have a value inasmuch that if you find the forecast charts showing swell from one direction and the waves from the opposite direction or even at right angles to the swell direction, then you should be aware that there will be a higher probability of so called freak waves, where wave and swell crests combine to produce more exceptional wave conditions. It may only be in more extreme weather conditions that you will be concerned about these peak combinations of sea and swell, but the point to remember is that the forecast charts do not take into account the combining effect of the sea and swell and the way in which they can enhance wave heights.

Forecasting Visibility

One of the most difficult areas for forecasters is to develop forecasts of visibility. Even with the advent of modern electronics for navigation, visual observations are still a vital part of navigation and particularly collision avoidance, so yachtsmen have a particular interest in visibility forecasts –

and yet developing accurate visibility forecasts is not easy. The visibility reduction caused by rain in frontal systems is relatively easy to forecast, and when you understand the rain patterns associated with frontal systems and the intensity of the system then it is relatively easy to get some idea of what sort of visibility can be expected. However, even here the density of rain and its effect on visibility can vary enormously; but fortunately rain rarely cuts down visibility to less than a mile except in very heavy local storms although it can affect radar performance. You are going to be more concerned with the effects of rain on your pleasure and comfort rather than on the visibility and it is the mist and fog which are much more likely to be of concern. There may be a fine line between persistent drizzle and mist in terms of the effects on visibility, but it is the actual range of visibility which can be difficult to forecast. If visibility is a mile, then navigation is not too difficult, but if it drops to half a mile then you can really be stretching your navigation resources, and the visual checks will come up with a suddenness which is not conducive to relaxed sailing.

Below half a mile you start getting into what is termed fog conditions. Fog is only caused through temperature variations in the atmosphere and on the land and sea. Moist, warm air hitting cold land or sea will produce fog, but trying to forecast the subtle temperature differences which will actually cause the fog to appear, and its density when it does, is a skilled art and there can be very local variations in these temperatures which can make fog very patchy and very local in its effect.

The weather charts that you receive on a weatherfax will not give you much in the way of information about the potential for fog conditions, and for forecasting fog you will normally have to rely on the radio weather forecasts. These are going to be vague in delineating the extent of fog, and will tend to resort to using phrases such as 'extensive fog patches', or 'fog patches', phrases which will put you on your guard as far as visibility is concerned, but do little to help you identify whether there will be fog in the particular area where you intend to be operating or trying to make a landfall. You can probably infer from a forecast which gives extensive fog, that you can expect it to be persistent and for it not to clear readily, whereas with a forecast of fog patches there is more hope that clearances will occur.

Local observation may help you to anticipate areas of fog and you can often see it coming up as a bank on the horizon or over the land, which can give you a degree of early warning. If you are in fog and you see the sun starting to shine through the overcast, then you can have a degree of hope that the fog will be clearing before long. There is a certain relationship between wind and fog which can help to give you a clue from the forecast charts. Certain types of fog conditions are obviously more prevalent in the light winds or calm conditions usually associated with high pressure, and they can often be associated with an occluded front or very weak frontal activity, but there is nothing positive about these indications. Fog can occur in quite strong wind conditions and a good example of this can be seen from the extensive fog often found on the

Grand Banks of Newfoundland.

Fog in more open sea such as that found on the Grand Banks of Newfoundland is more easy to infer from the forecast charts, provided charts of sea temperature are available. With a warm, moist wind blowing over a colder sea, then fog is a distinct possibility, and in open sea areas you have more consistent conditions which are easier to forecast. Close to land the temperature variations can be much more local, making them much harder to forecast reliably and so there is very little you can infer from the forecast charts or the forecasts themselves, except to be on your guard when fog patches are forecast. Fog and visibility are probably the main areas where you are best simply to rely on what the forecasts suggest, because there is not too much that you can do to improve on these forecasts to get a better indication of what might be occurring in your particular locality.

Improving the Forecast
As far as the wind and sea conditions are concerned there is a great deal that you can do to improve on the quality of transmitted forecasts. If you take a weather chart or better still a series of weather charts and combine these with the broadcast weather forecast and your own visual observations about what is going on, together with a knowledge of the coastal topography and tides, then you are in a position to fine-tune the forecast and generate specific forecasts for your own requirements. It is the weather charts which provide the key to this method of interpreting and enhancing the weather forecast quality, because these weather charts show the forecast of the way in which the general weather pattern is developing. It is changes in the pressure systems and their associated fronts which will trigger most of the changes in the weather conditions and it is largely by your interpretation of when these changes in the weather patterns and frontal systems will reach your particular locality that you can put a much more precise timing on the changes contained in the general weather forecast. This timing can then be confirmed by visual observation, so that you can make your sailing plans with a much greater degree of confidence.

To enable you to carry out this fine-tuning of the weather forecast you need two consecutive weather charts. These weather charts should be on the largest scale available covering the area which you are in. Weather charts generally cover a considerable area of the globe. For instance one chart might cover much of the northern Atlantic and can be useful for showing what is coming in from the west if you are in Britain. However, for the purposes of developing your own forecast, you then want to get a larger scale weather chart, perhaps one just covering the British Isles, where the positions of the frontal systems and isobars can be seen with greater accuracy in relation to your present or proposed position. The two charts you need may be 12 or 24 hours apart in terms of timing, and probably the 24 hour interval is adequate for most requirements. The charts you use should have the isobars plotted at 4 mb intervals because at this scale of plotting much more detail about the shape and scale of

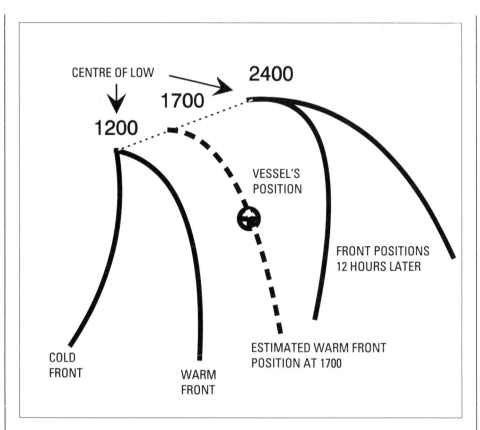

Estimating the movement of fronts relative to a yacht's position.

weather systems can be determined and local features become more obvious.

If you take the earlier chart, which could be one of the actual weather pattern some few hours previously rather than a forecast chart, and transfer the position of the centres of pressure – whether high or low – and the position of the associated frontal systems from the 24 hour chart on to the current chart, then you will immediately be able to compare the relative positions of the two weather patterns. This direct comparison will enable you to appreciate the changes which are forecast to occur over the 24 hour period.

Now you have two choices about how you proceed, one being to divide up the space between the two lines of the frontal system and draw in a series of lines suggesting where the centre of the depression and its associated fronts would be every 6 hours or so. Alternatively you can draw in the line of the front through your current position, and then establish the time when it would pass through this position by measuring the relative distances on each side of this line to the plotted positions of the front at the known times of the two charts you are using.

WEATHER FORECASTS

When Will the Weather Break?

The diagram will make this clearer, but the object in either case is to be able to determine with a reasonable degree of accuracy the time at which the frontal line will pass your position or a position in which you are particularly interested. Once you can establish this time then this will give you the key to what the weather will be doing at any given time and also the time when anticipated changes in the weather will occur. Remember when making any assessment about changes that the frontal line you have plotted is the junction between the warm and cold air masses *at the surface* and some changes may occur before or after this line.

As an alternative to using paper weather charts for this purpose you could use the sequential weather charts shown on TV. If you record these and then play them back as a freeze frame sequence you should be able to establish quite closely when a front will pass through your location. Provided you have the right quality of TV weather chart which shows the fronts and which puts a timing on the charts then this can be a useful way of establishing when changes will occur in your locality.

From the plotted line you will be able to measure the speed of advance of the frontal system in relation to your position and from this you will be able to gauge with a considerable degree of accuracy the time at which the changes in the weather conditions associated with the front will pass through your position or across your proposed track. Obviously from such a plot you are making the assumption that the frontal system is making steady progress and is not erratic, but even with erratic movement the timing is not likely to be more than a couple of hours out which would be generally acceptable.

You may be able to refine this timing with visual observations which will announce the arrival of the frontal system, by changes in cloud patterns together with the advent of rain, or change in the rain pattern, or a switch to rain showers, which will give you further confirmation of your personalised forecast; but of course the actual weather changes will be occurring as you get these clues. What you really want as far as the weather is concerned is prior knowledge and this is what transferring the lines and positions on the weather charts can give you.

Some Unpredictable Situations

Obviously there are going to be weather situations where this method of interpreting the forecast charts will not always be enough to give you such a straightforward ability to forecast change. The angle of advance of a weather front may mean that the line of the front actually stays over your position or track. This can occur when a front has curled round and lies on or nearly on an east–west direction. In this situation it may require only a comparatively small movement of the front one way or the other to make a significant change in the weather and the accuracy of the plot may not be enough to indicate this. However at least you will be aware of the situation and you will know what any observed changes in the weather will indicate.

Another situation which may make life difficult in terms of anticipating weather changes can occur if the centre of a depression is forecast to pass over or close to your position. Once again a comparatively small variation in the position of the centre of a depression can make a significant difference in the weather conditions, particularly the wind direction. The weather forecaster is likely to hedge his bets quite considerably in such a situation because he is dealing with quite large forecast areas, but with your plot you will have a much clearer picture of the situation as far as your particular position is concerned. Even if the changes in wind direction do not occur exactly as planned, at least you will know what is going on and be in a better position to anticipate future changes.

From this you should be able to appreciate the vital role which weather charts can play in improving the quality of weather forecasts to focus on your particular situation. The weather forecasters do their best within the limits of a verbal forecast, but you have to appreciate the constraints of time and space available in which they have to get the message across, as well as the large areas of sea for which they are generating forecasts. Most forecasts that you receive cannot be specific to your particular requirements but if you take the trouble to get weather charts and personalise them in the ways suggested, then you can take on the forecasting role where the professional forecaster leaves off.

Once you have a more accurate timing for changes in the weather, you are then in a position to look at these changes in relation to your local sea area and see how local conditions such as headlands, narrow channels and tides could affect the general forecast. In this way you will have generated your own weather forecast which should prove considerably superior to that broadcast by radio.

4 Weather Patterns

In trying to visualise the weather patterns in four dimensions, it helps a great deal to have a basic understanding of how the highs and lows are formed, what makes the weather patterns move and change, and how the 'engine' of the atmosphere operates. The term 'engine' is used because there is a tremendous amount of energy locked in the atmosphere. This gets released in a variety of ways, such as wind, rain and lightning, and understanding how this 'engine' works and how it utilises its energy is an important step towards understanding the weather and knowing what the weather is going to do.

It is the sun which provides the energy for the atmospheric engine, and the basic circulation of the atmosphere is based around the principle that hotter air rises and cooler air sinks. The sun's warmth is much more intense around the equator area than it is at the poles, and so the basic circulation of the atmosphere consists of the air rising around the equator and then flowing at high level northward or southward towards the poles where it gradually cools and sinks, and then this cool air flows on the surface of the earth back towards the equator. The weather would be quite a simple matter to predict if this ideal flow of air was maintained but there is a large number of other factors which have to be taken into account when trying to assess the weather patterns.

Temperature Variations

Some of these factors operate in the very short term and a good example of this is thunderstorms, when the effect is both relatively short term and local. Other factors operate on a daily basis and these are usually due to the variation in temperatures of land surfaces between night and day under the influence of the sun's heating. Then there are the seasonal changes which are mainly due to the differential heating by the sun which has a stronger heating power when it is directly overhead than when the its rays are striking the earth at an angle. The seasonal change is a result of the sun being overhead north or south of the equator at different seasons and the difference in heating effect is marked by the changes from summer to winter.

One of the major factors involved in day to day weather effects is the different rates at which land and sea absorb the heat from the sun and thus change the temperature. This sort of effect in a local form is responsible for land and sea breezes and other local phenomena such as some types of fog, but there are also global effects created by the differential heating of large land and sea masses. Then there is the effect of a cloudy day which reduces the amount of the sun's heat getting to the earth underneath and this again can create variations in temperature or in many cases reduce the variations in temperature between different areas, a fact which can be noticed by the less volatile weather situations which tend to occur on days when it is cloudy. In order to help understand this

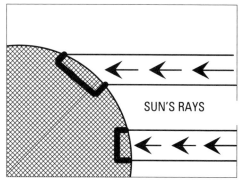

The heating of the earth by the sun's rays is an important element in weather development. This diagram shows how the heating at the equator is more intense than further north or south because the heat is concentrated over a smaller area of the earth's surface.

complex weather picture it can help to try and visualise the temperatures converted into pressures, with the colder air generally relating to areas of high pressure and the warmer air to areas of low pressure. Colder air is more dense hence the higher atmospheric pressure and if you adopt this approach and start to see the world air circulation in terms of pressure then it is easier to relate it to the weather charts which show the weather patterns as highs and lows. When looking at atmospheric pressures, remember that the air flow will tend to be from the high pressure to the low pressure on the surface of the earth because nature wants to get everything on an even balance – though as far as the weather is concerned, she rarely succeeds.

The Coriolis Force

If the different rates of heating over various time scales and the consequent effects on atmospheric pressure were not enough to complicate the weather picture, another factor which comes into the general weather assessment and makes things hard to understand is the Coriolis force. We have already seen the idealised air flow over the earth, where the air rises at the equator and the colder air flows down from the poles to replace this rising warm air. This lower, colder air flows towards the equator because the pressure is higher at the poles where the air is colder and thus more dense; and with lower pressure at the equator, the air flows down what is termed a pressure gradient. In theory this should be a steady flow but the Coriolis force comes into effect on this air flow and causes the flow to deviate from the straight path down the pressure slope. The Coriolis force is created by the earth's rotation and what in effect happens is that it is not actually the air flowing north or south from the poles which changes, but the earth underneath the air which rotates and which thus gives the effect that the air flow has been deflected. If you plotted a particular point in the air flow, say a balloon very close to the surface, then you would find that the longitude of this balloon changes as well as its latitude as it heads south in the air flow. This Coriolis deflection or force increases towards the poles because the longitude there changes much more quickly for a given distance.

We see the effect of this Coriolis force in many of the prevailing winds around the world. The trade winds are a good example of how the Coriolis force serves to deviate the north/south flow of the general direction of the wind. These trade winds tend to occur nearer the equator, but further north in the temperate zones, the winds tend to be south westerly in the northern hemisphere and north westerly in the southern hemisphere. Here we are looking at the effect of the Coriolis force on world weather patterns but it also has an influence on more local wind patterns. We will see later that it has to be taken into account when trying to forecast the wind patterns around a low or high pressure area.

So what we end up with is still the basic low pressure at the equator and high pressure at the poles, but the wind adopting a spiralling effect as it flows from the poles along the surface towards the equator. This would still make life fairly simple in terms of forecasting if this were all we had to contend with, but unfortunately the warmer air rising at the equator starts to cool long before it gets to the poles, forming an area of high pressure around 35 degrees north and an area of low pressure around 60 degrees north. It is these secondary circulations which tend to form the prevailing north east trades in the lower latitudes, and the prevailing westerlies or south westerlies in higher latitudes.

Land and Sea

The system becomes even more complicated when you have to take into account the very uneven distribution of land and sea around the world. We have already noted that the land tends to warm up more quickly and have higher temperatures than the sea under the influence of the heating from the sun. It also cools more extensively at night or in the winter months whilst the sea keeps a more even temperature. This means that the air over land areas is heated more in the summer months which produces areas of low pressure over the land whilst high pressure tends to form over the cooler sea areas. In the winter this situation is reversed to a certain extent with the land areas being colder than the sea, and so high pressure tends to form over land areas in contrast to lower pressures over sea areas. This is a very broad generalisation of what happens because there are so many interrelated side effects, but a good example of this can be seen with the Azores High, which fills much of the Atlantic Ocean between 25 degrees and 50 degrees north in the summer months and which is a fairly consistent weather feature.

Adding to the confusion is the fact that the earth's axis in relation to

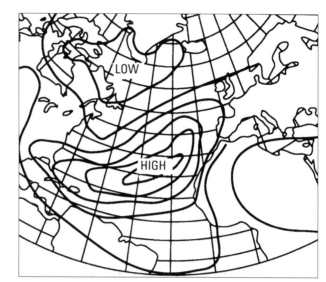

In the summer months the Azores High moves north and often provides a block in the path of the Atlantic depressions which are then forced further north.

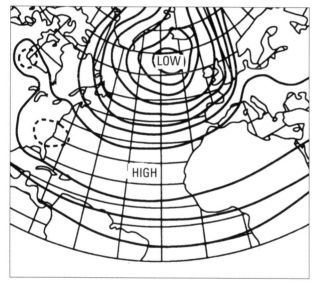

In the winter the Azores High moves south, allowing the depressions which sweep across the Atlantic also to move south, bringing the typically stronger winds.

the sun changes between summer and winter. In effect this means that the sun is directly overhead at $23^{1}/_{2}$ degrees north at midday during the northern hemisphere summer, rather than at the equator. When the sun is overhead the heating of the land and the sea is obviously more intense and so the broad weather patterns we have illustrated tend to move north and south with the seasons. Using the Azores High as an example here, it tends to move north during the summer months tending to push the run of low pressure areas which are a feature of the higher latitudes further north, so that strong winds associated with these depressions are less frequent in the summer months. In the winter months the Azores High tends to sink further south, so that these depressions can whistle across the Atlantic at 40 degrees or 45 degrees north, rather than the 50 degrees or 60 degrees north found in the summer months.

So we have these broad weather patterns, and it can be seen from the diagrams that these represent the relatively stable and predictable situation which might exist if it weren't for a great deal of local complication which comes into the weather. If the weather stuck to these tidy patterns it would be easy to forecast and we wouldn't suffer the rapid short term changes which can be a feature of weather in temperate regions. Some areas of the world have very predictable and established weather patterns and this is particularly the case with the north east and south east trade winds which blow very consistently from the same direction, although they can vary considerably in strength. The problems occurring in the weather patterns start when we get a fairly consistent wind blowing from one direction, meeting a fairly consistent wind blowing from a different direction.

Wind Flow Around the World
If you look at the diagram showing the general wind flow around the world, then you will see that one of these belts where conflicting winds can meet exists around the equator, and another one in the temperate latitudes from around 45 degrees to 60 degrees north or south. Where the north east trades and south east trade winds meet around the equator area, the mixing of the winds is relatively gentle because the different winds are

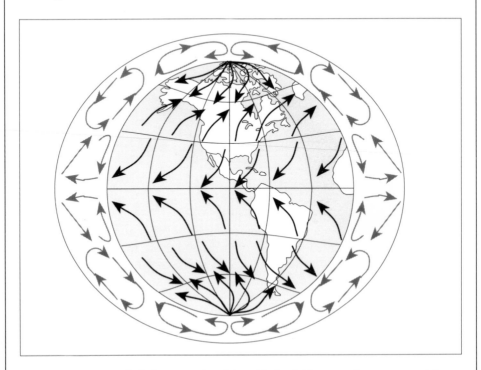

The general pattern of winds across the globe with the doldrums at the equator and the polar front at around 50 degrees north and south.

approaching each other at an angle of approximately 90 degrees. This mixing area – which is called the doldrums – is notable for its thunderstorms and periods of calm and its generally unpredictable winds because in this mixing area, or buffer zone, both the trade winds are swept on to a more westerly track, and this allows the winds to mix without the sort of turbulence which in turn can result in the more extreme weather conditions. In the doldrums the two air flows which are mixing also have a way out because the air here is getting warmer and so tends to rise. Generally speaking the doldrums are notable for their lack of wind rather than for their extreme conditions.

In the temperate latitudes where the winds mix you find the south westerly wind running out from the band of high pressure which circles the globe at 30 degrees to 50 degrees north. These winds meet the cold north easterly winds which run outwards from the polar high pressure areas, and here at the meeting point in the temperate latitudes, you have these two opposing winds meeting head-on in a clash which can generate some of the most violent weather in the world.

The difference in temperature between these two opposing winds is a very important factor. At the meeting point at the equator at the doldrums the winds which merge into the westerlies are winds of very similar temperature, which helps to prevent any violent interaction. In the temperate latitudes the cold, mainly dry north easterly winds flowing down from the polar regions meet up with the warm, moist south westerlies so not only is there a clash in wind direction, but there is also a clash of temperatures, and it is these temperature differences which can provide much of the energy to fuel the formation of deep depressions which are a feature of these regions.

Mixing Cold and Warm Waters
As these two opposing winds meet they tend to get deflected, with the north easterlies flowing from the polar regions switching round to become more easterly, and the south westerlies flowing in a more westerly direction. So you have the cold easterly winds flowing in the northern sector, and warmer, moister westerly winds in the more southerly sector – but unfortunately winds cannot flow in opposite directions alongside each other without a strong interaction. You can see the type of effect generated by these opposing flows of air if you try and visualise two opposing flows of water. This is apparent in some tidal races where there may be just a different speed between two water flows rather than having them flow in opposite directions, but the resulting interaction can be quite ferocious. The characteristics of such interaction are the whirlpools which are generated, spinning round with a depressed central area. Such whirlpools are a characteristic of any meeting point where two fluids flow in opposite directions, and you can see similar effects occurring in the Gulf Stream, particularly where it meets the Labrador Current heading in the opposite direction off the eastern coast of North America.

Now, going back to the two bodies of air flowing in opposite directions in the temperate latitudes, you get a very strong interaction between these two opposing flows. They start to intermix and form a type of whirlpool, known in the language of the weather as a depression. Here you have the characteristic formations of the main weather patterns which are found in the temperate latitudes.

This area where the cold polar air meets the warmer air coming from the south is known as the polar front. Frontal systems are an important feature of any weather system and are the meeting point of cold and warm air masses. This polar front differs from the frontal systems which tend to be found on weather maps and which form part of the structure of a depression mainly because the air masses at the polar front are moving in opposite directions. Going back to the analogy with the water flow, the energy for the water to generate eddies and whirlpools comes from the fact that the water is flowing downhill.

In the atmosphere there is a certain amount of energy contained in the air masses which are moving, but there is a lot more energy in the latent heat available in the moisture which is contained in the air. When cold and warm air meet, much of this latent heat is released in the form of rain, and this release of energy contributes to the formation of the embryo depressions which are forming as eddies in the two opposing flows. With this supply of energy these eddies or whirlpools can deepen and grow and can become major features of the weather pattern, sometimes extending over thousands of miles of ocean. Depressions can vary enormously in shape and form and in some cases they can be very extensive while in others quite local, maybe just 100 miles or so across. They can persist for several days or they can be more transient and no two weather systems are likely to be the same, so that the interaction between these two air masses becomes an extremely complex relationship, one which can be very difficult to forecast. This interaction between the two air masses, one cold and one warm, takes place in three dimensions because the warm air will tend to rise over the colder air and it is not always easy to appreciate this three dimensional picture of the weather from its two dimensional portrayal on weather maps.

The polar front itself tends to be portrayed as a nice tidy line running round the earth at around 55 degrees or 60 degrees north or south. In an ideal situation this might probably be the case but its position can vary a great deal once you take into account the effects of the different heating or cooling of the air over land masses. Particularly in the northern hemisphere there are large land masses at this latitude and in the summer these get heated more than the adjacent seas, whilst in the winter they are colder. These variations in heating or cooling will affect the patterns of air flow to quite a considerable degree. The air also tends to be drier over large continental areas because air will only pick up moisture when it passes over the sea. This means that there is less moisture involved in the two opposing air flows which meet at the polar front over land which in turn means that there is less energy available to perpetuate or develop the depressions which might form.

How Depressions Start

Over land the depressions or eddies which are generated by the interaction of these two air flows tend to be less severe. However if these depressions then move out over the water, they can start to pick up energy as they come in contact with moist airflows coming up from the south. This is why you will often see quite mild looking depressions setting out from the east coast of North America and becoming more vigorous as they head out across the Atlantic. The same sort of situation occurs in the Pacific, and almost invariably the track of these depressions formed at the polar front is eastward because the depressions themselves tend to be formed to the south of the polar front where they get forced into the less dense, warmer, moister air which is a feature of the side of the polar front away from the poles.

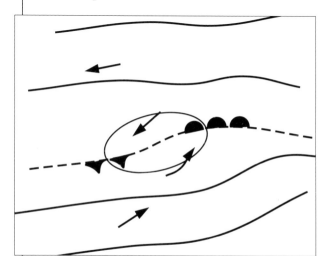

The early stages of the formation of a depression as the warm and cold air mix in turbulence along the polar front.

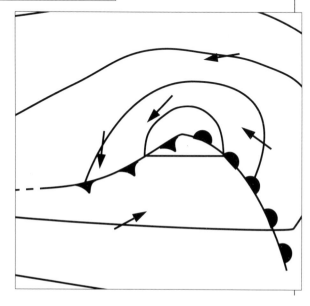

A further stage in the development of a depression as the circular motion becomes established and the warm and cold fronts establish a positive identity.

A fully formed depression with the sharp change in wind direction seen along the line of the fronts.

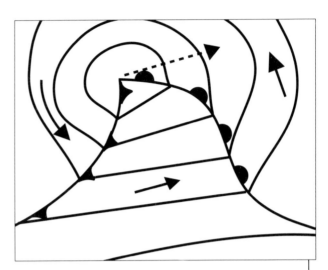

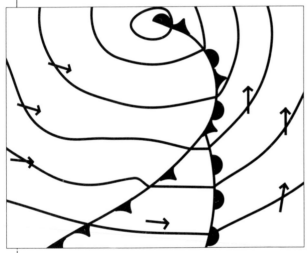

The closing stages of a typical depression where the cold front has caught up the warm front. The depression will now start to fill and become less intense.

The actual formation of a depression starts by the interaction of the cold and warm air flows. We can visualise these two opposing air flows as testing each other out by making small incursions into the opposing flow, and so they are first seen as a small deflection in the polar front. The activity in this frontal area is occurring in three dimensions with the warmer, moister air tending to lift and rise over the colder, drier polar air. So we find the colder air starting to come in under the warmer air, and gradually the two air flows start to embrace one another and a circular motion is set up which is the embryo depression. The front which represents the dividing line between the cold and warm air takes some time to be swung round from its main east–west axis. Indeed while the winds start to flow in the circular pattern typical of a depression, the actual frontal systems marking the dividing line between the different air flows move much more slowly. The speed of the wind associated with a depression does not signify that the associated frontal systems are moving at the same speed. It can take two or three days before the once straight line front separating the polar air and the warmer air from the south bends right round and they join up and become occluded. The occluded front is one where the cold air has come round full circle and caught up with the cold air in front, squeezing the remaining warmer air into higher altitudes – this usually signifies that the depression is weakening and coming near the end of its life.

Lows and Highs

The weather maps show the weather patterns in terms of isobars, that is, lines of equal pressure. It has been found that there is a strong relationship between the atmospheric pressure and the pattern of air flow so that these two dimensional weather maps are the best way to show what is happening. We tend to look at depressions, or areas of low pressure, in isolation because they are such significant features on any weather map. They have their counterparts in anti-cyclones or areas of high pressure which can have somewhat similar characteristics. There are significant differences between the two apart from the atmospheric pressure. Much more significant from the sailor's point of view is the air flow around the systems, with depressions having an anti-clockwise airflow and anti-cyclones having a clockwise air flow in the northern hemisphere. These directions are reversed in the southern hemisphere. Another important difference is that whilst depressions are associated with active frontal systems which generate different weather conditions in different sectors of the depression, anti-cyclones do not generally have frontal systems associated with them or, if there are frontal systems running into an anti-cyclone, then these tend to be the tail end of low pressure frontal systems. We tend to look at depressions and anti-cyclones in terms of their barometric pressure because that is the way they are defined on two dimensional weather charts, but the temperatures associated with different sectors of these systems can also be significant. But probably of most interest and concern to yachts are the wind flows around these systems and this will be looked at in the next chapter in much more detail.

The absence of frontal systems in anti-cyclones or high pressure areas tends to produce more stable weather conditions and more consistent wind and weather. High pressure areas tend to be more persistent and depressions more transient, so anti-cyclones are slower moving and indeed often remain stationary for considerable periods. The absence of any frontal systems tends to reduce the amount of cloud found in these areas and without the mix of warm moist air and cold air there is much less energy in anti-cyclones. In general then, high pressure areas are associated with fine consistent weather, whereas low pressure areas tend to be the harbingers of bad weather, both wind and rain.

It is the steep gradient between higher pressure and lower pressure in a depression which tends to generate the wind. The air will always tend to flow towards areas of low pressure, and it might be expected that the air would flow directly in towards the centre of a depression. However, rather like water flowing down a plug hole it tends to follow a circular path following the contour lines of the isobars and only slightly canted in towards the centre. It is this circular flow which generates the stronger winds associated with depressions, and the closer the spacing of the isobars, the stronger the winds. However because the depression is initially formed along a frontal line between cold air and warm air, the activity in a depression is much more complex than that associated with water just running down a plug hole.

Once again we have to come back to trying to look at a depression in three dimensions because within the circular flow of the depression the warm air is climbing up and over the colder air, a movement which generates its own area of activity. These frontal areas tend to have characteristic weather features which not only produce some of the most intense weather associated with a depression, but also have the beneficial characteristics of allowing an observer to identify and measure the progress of the depression, and thus help to forecast future weather conditions. Frontal systems can have their own characteristic cloud patterns and the rainfall which is associated with the different types of cloud can also give a clue as to what is going on, so while the fronts may have a down side in terms of the weather they produce, they do have an up side in terms of the information they can give.

Cloud conditions associated with the warm sector of a depression. This is part of a very active Atlantic depression when the wind was blowing Force 10.

Three Types of Front

There are three main types of front. A warm front is one where the warm air is overtaking the cold air in front of it. Then there is the cold front where cold air is overtaking warm air; and thirdly there is the occluded front where the cold front has caught up with the warm front so that at sea level it is a question of cold air overtaking the cold air in front of it with the warm air pushed up above sea level. There are two types of occluded front, the cold occlusion, which is the commoner type where colder air is overtaking cold air with the warm air above, and the warm occlusion where cold air is overtaking colder air again with the warm air above.

It is worth looking at each of these types of frontal system in considerable detail because of the profound effect they have on weather and potential changes in the weather. All frontal systems tend to be areas of considerable weather activity with notable changes in temperature, pressure, wind and moisture. The cold front and the warm front tend to be the most active and show the most pronounced changes, and in general the more active the front, the more quickly it moves. Occluded fronts tend to be less active and slower moving, and the weather changes associated with such fronts tend to be less vigorous, although occluded fronts can have a pronounced effect on visibility because of the drizzle, mist or fog which is often associated with them.

Warm Fronts

A warm front is where the warmer air is overtaking and rising above the colder air in front of it. Now the warmer air contains a considerable amount of moisture, at least in contrast to the colder air above which it is rising. The warm moist air coming into contact with the cold air causes the warm air to be cooled which in turn tends to release the moisture in the form of rain or snow. This rain, which can be heavy at times, is one of the characteristic features of a warm front. Another characteristic feature of the approach of a warm front is the gradual lowering of the cloud base as the frontal line approaches. The first warning signs of the approach of a warm front could be 300–400 miles before the actual surface division

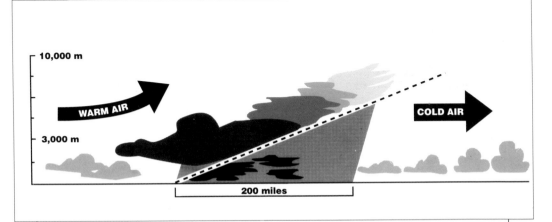

Cross section of a typical warm front with the warmer air coming in over the cold air and forming clouds along the border line turbulence. The clouds tend to get heavier and lower as the front nears sea level and the rain starts with the heavier cloud.

WEATHER PATTERNS

between the warm and cold air, and these will be seen as high cirrus clouds which mark the upper edge of the warm air which is rising above the cold air. These cirrus clouds could be 30,000 feet above sea level and from this high point the line of the front will angle down to sea level, with the cloud getting steadily denser and lower as the line of the approaching front gets closer. From the cirrus cloud the cloud will thicken into cirrostratus and then into heavier altostratus. It is with the approach of these types of cloud that the first signs of rain are likely to start, and this could be at a point perhaps 200 miles ahead of the sea level front. From altostratus the cloud will drop into heavy and dark nimbostratus cloud along the line of the front, but this may well be obscured by lower dark stratus cloud as the rain gets heavier and visibility reduces. Because of the reduced visibility and the low cloud layer, it will be difficult to get any visible indication of the movement of the front, and it is only when the stratus cloud starts to disappear and the nimbostratus above starts to become apparent and the rain starts to ease that you will know that the front is nearly past, and that you can shortly expect clearer skies with more patchy cloud. However the overcast may well continue and although we have tried to describe here a typical warm front, there is nothing certain about the sequence of events and weather changes as the front goes through. The sequence and pattern of changes will depend to a considerable extent on the relative temperatures of the two air masses, the amount of moisture locked up in the warm air and the relative speeds of movement.

The actual extent of frontal weather you might experience at a particular point will also vary, depending on the direction from which the front is approaching. Normally frontal systems approach from a westerly direction both in the north and south hemispheres, but because the line of a front is often considerably curved, it could pass over your position at a considerable angle to the anticipated west to east direction, and this angular passage will considerably prolong your exposure to the effects of the front. Fronts also move in direct relationship to the depression of which they are a part, and whilst most depressions tend to move from west to east, quite a few will swing in a north easterly or south easterly direction, so here again the passage of the front over the particular position can vary considerably in terms of time.

Another factor which will affect the duration of the passage of a warm front, is the angle between the relative masses of cold and warm air. Typically this is quite a shallow angle, perhaps rising at 20 degrees from the horizontal, but it could be at a steeper angle, up to say 40 degrees, in which case the passage of the front will be notably quicker, and the sequence of changes will also be that much quicker.

There will be less activity towards the tail end of the front, where it reaches the edge of the depression and starts to fade; here the distance from front to back of the weather effects may be reduced to 100 miles compared with the 300 miles or more which might be expected with a fully active sector of the front.

Heavy showery clouds typical of those found after the passage of a cold front.

Cold Fronts

With a cold front the cold air is overtaking the warm air in front, but the transition from one air mass to the other tends to be much sharper, with the division following a near horizontal line at sea level and rising up in a steep curve as the cold air forces its way under the moist air. This means that instead of a gradual approach and change of conditions, a cold front would tend to approach as a thick bank of cloud as the first indication of the change. Even this thick black cloud may be obscured if there are overcast conditions in the warm air sector, and so the first indication you may have of the approach of the cold front is heavy rain. This heavy rainfall will continue until the sea level front has passed and then you can expect a fairly rapid clearance, signalled by broken cloud which is often followed by a hard duck-egg blue sky, a feature of the conditions found in the colder air after the passage of a cold front.

Compared with the 6 to 8 hours which it might take for a warm front to pass a given point, a cold front could pass within an hour or two and its

The towering active clouds of a cold front receding to give way to showery conditions.

Heavy black clouds typical of the final stages of a cold front when the rain has stopped and the clearance is starting.

effects might extend for only 50 miles. Just as with warm fronts there can be a considerable difference between one cold front and another, but the typical element is always the very vigorous activity resulting from the near vertical separation between the warm and cold air masses.

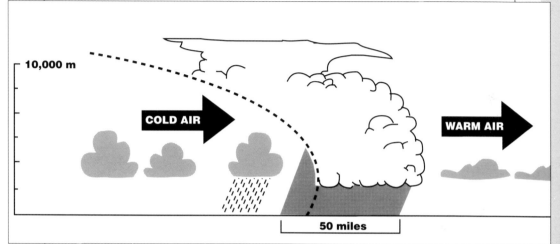

Cross section of a typical cold front with the colder air pushing under the warmer air, producing the towering clouds typical of the cold front, with the showers from the cumulus clouds following behind.

Occluded Fronts

Warm fronts generally travel at a speed of somewhere around fifteen knots, whilst cold fronts average around twenty knots. These speeds can obviously vary but in general cold fronts will move faster than warm fronts. You can see this with the development of a depression and the way in which the fronts move in relation to each other. It is obvious that with the speed differential between the two frontal systems, the cold front will inevitably catch up with the warm front. This will happen towards the centre of the depression initially, and this will form what is called an occluded front. Provided that the life of the depression is long enough, this occluded front will extend further and further out from the centre as the warm and cold fronts merge. The advent of the occluded frontal system is often a sign that the depression itself is reaching the end of its life and will start to fill, and this occurs partly because the latent heat which is released when the water vapour condenses to form rain or snow is no longer available in the frontal system to help generate the energy necessary to perpetuate it. So occluded fronts are generally notable for being less active than warm or cold fronts, and typically they generate light rain or drizzle with no clear-cut sharp changes in weather.

Typically an occlusion consists of one lot of cold air catching up another lot of cold air, which forces the warm air which was previously between the two to rise above sea level. Obviously this warm air, if it contains moisture, will still release this moisture in the form of rain or drizzle as it rises, but by this time much of the moisture has probably already been drained from the warm air and certainly as it rises it gets colder and there is less activity in this type of occluded front. Where colder air is overtaking cold air and forcing the warm air upwards, then the weather changes in the occluded front are likely to be a weakened version of those experienced in a cold front; whereas if colder air is being overtaken by cold air with the warm air being forced upwards, then the weather will be more akin to that found in a warm front, but again much weaker. For the meteorologists there are probably significant differences to be found in these two types of occlusion, but for the yachtsman there is really little need to differentiate between them, the main point being that the changes associated with such a frontal system are comparatively innocuous and there are unlikely to be any sudden changes in wind direction or strength, although the rain or drizzle can affect visibility.

At the tail end of an occluded front when the warm and cold fronts have linked up for almost their entire length, then the passage of an occluded front may hardly be noticed except by cloudy skies. Any changes in the weather associated with this weakened occluded front will be very gradual and gentle, and the wind conditions are also likely to be comparatively mild.

Secondary Lows
After a depression is a few days old, and when it may have become quite large and slow moving, it is not unusual to find that the fronts have become increasingly twisted around the centre and they can trail away in a long line, something like the tail of a comet. Although the weather pattern may look comparatively harmless it is often along this frontal line or trough that a small wave depression can form. It has to be remembered that this frontal line is in fact the new location of the polar front, although it is not always easy to recognise in its distorted form at surface level. This secondary depression forming along the front can pick up some of the residual energy left in the front. It is not unusual for this secondary depression to develop quite rapidly and to gain speed as it draws in moist warm air to renew its energy, and often it will run along the line of the trough and join up with its dying parent to renew the activity. Secondary lows can also form along very active cold fronts because here you can have very sudden changes in wind direction, perhaps up to 120 degrees or more, meaning that you have winds flowing in two almost opposing directions, and one lot of air is warm and one lot cold, giving almost a repeat of the sort of conditions which form a low along the polar front. These secondary depressions are more likely to form along very active cold fronts where there is a lot of energy available in the form of latent heat, and they can form and develop very quickly which means that they may not be detected on longer term forecasts. The Fastnet gale of 1979 was one such secondary low which developed and moved quickly east

within 24 hours. This type of very active secondary depression tends to be a phenomenon found in the summer months rather than during the winter months when the main depressions are much more active and mature.

Inconsistencies

So far we have looked at the general pattern of highs and lows and the frontal systems associated with them, but you have to appreciate that these weather systems are never static. Whilst in the areas of the trade winds, and around some of the big oceanic highs such as the Azores High, the weather conditions may be very stable and can be relied on day after day to produce reasonably consistent conditions, this is rarely the case in the temperate latitudes. Here the pressure systems and their associated frontal systems are in a constant state of flux and it is rare for two weather patterns to be exactly the same. This is what can make the forecaster's job so difficult and before the advent of the computer it was the weather forecasters' experience in knowing the behaviour of weather patterns which was largely responsible for the quality of the output of the forecast. The very advanced computer programs which are now used for weather forecasting still take into account the previous movement and development of weather patterns, but it should be remembered that the raw information fed into these computer programs may not always be as complete as would be liked. Whilst observations of existing weather over land areas can be complete and precise, observations from ocean areas are far less frequent and can often be more subjective. One of the problems here is that weather features which are in the process of early development may not always be detectable because of the scarcity of observations in that area. The only consolation here is that features over the ocean tend to be more consistent than those over land, largely because there are fewer features such as local heating of land masses which will distort the general pattern.

Whilst we try and look for consistency and regular behaviour in the weather patterns that we see from the forecast charts, we also have to be prepared for the unexpected. The nice regular spacing of isobars around a depression or an anti-cyclone appears to present a clear picture of regular wind behaviour, but you have to remember that those isobars have been drawn by the computer which does tend to average out the features. However the computer is also on the lookout for abnormalities because it is these which tend to produce unexpected or short term changes in the weather. As a yachtsman you have to rely to a large degree on the forecasts you get because you will not have enough information at your finger tips to develop a logical argument against it. However, if you have this understanding of how weather systems are formed and how they develop and die, then at least you will be in a better position to appreciate what forecasters are trying to tell you, and you will also be able to relate what you see to the general weather patterns. This we will look at in later chapters, but now we come on to the subject which is of prime importance to yachts, and that is the wind.

5 Predicting Winds

For sailors wind is one of the most important considerations when assessing the weather, and as we have already seen it is not always the easiest thing to predict accurately. In a sailboat wind is of primary importance because it is your main propulsion power but as the wind gets stronger it can also have a very important effect on your safety. Most yacht skippers will appreciate the very significant difference between a Force 6 and a Force 8 wind, one being a very invigorating sailing wind and the other being the situation where you shorten sail and start thinking about seeking shelter or even employing survival tactics. In a powerboat, the wind itself does not have such an immediate effect on performance but it is the effect of the wind on the sea which can have a considerable influence on progress and eventually, as the wind gets stronger, on safety. In some respects a powerboat is more sensitive to wind conditions because it will probably be quite happy in winds of Force 8 in sea areas in the lee of the land and which are well sheltered so that the sea does not have a chance to build up, whereas a sailboat in the same circumstances will still have to think very seriously about shortening sail.

No-one will doubt the primary effect of the wind on all types of yacht and the easy solution is simply to listen to the forecast, believe every word of it and make your decisions accordingly. To do so can lead to either an over cautious approach to yachting or a very aggrieved feeling when the wind turns

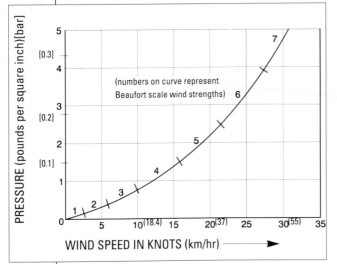

(numbers on curve represent Beaufort scale wind strengths)

The wind can exert a considerable pressure, and this graph shows how the pressure varies with wind strength. With winds of Force 7 the pressure can be between 4 lb and 6 lb per sq in.

out to be stronger or lighter than the forecast suggests. It is very easy to blame the forecasters in these situations, but it is quite rare for the forecasters to get things wrong. When you find the wind different from what the forecast has suggested, then this is usually a failure on your part to fine-tune the forecast to your particular requirements. Without this fine-tuning you will always be in for surprises, some good and some bad, and it is a very unseamanlike approach to yachting if you just take the forecast as gospel and don't try to understand it.

Seeing the Wind

Following on from the last chapter, we must now look at weather patterns in more detail. In order to do this we must have a better understanding of just what the wind is and how it behaves. We are immediately at a disadvantage here because we can't see the wind. The wind can be likened to a fluid just like water or other liquids but with the big difference that firstly the wind is much lighter or less dense than water, and secondly the air is invisible and therefore you cannot see the wind and how it is behaving. You can certainly see the effects of the wind, and no yachtsman will be in any doubt that you can feel its effects. There are a few occasions when you can 'see' the wind, such as when smoke is coming from a chimney or in fog. In these situations where a visible gas is mixed with the invisible air, you not only have a visible recognition of the wind but you can also see more clearly the way it behaves.

The thing you will notice with wind coming out of a chimney is that the mixed air and gasses very rarely flow in a steady straight line. The smoke swirls and boils about as it mixes with the air, some parts of the smoke moving slowly, others quickly, part of it twisting and turning. Apart from the general direction of flow the behaviour of the smoke appears to be turbulent and random. The only situation where this might not be true is in very light winds when smoke is rising almost vertically and moving slowly, and then the unpredictable movements and the turbulence are greatly reduced. The stronger the wind, the more active the various movements within the smoke flow, and here we have one of the keys to the behaviour of the wind itself.

Air Turbulence

The smoke eddies and flows about partly because it is usually warmer than the air with which it is mixing, but also because when you introduce the secondary stream of smoke into the main air flow, it takes time for the two flows of fluid to mix. There is a further complication in the process in which the general air flow approaching the chimney is broken up to a certain extent by the chimney itself, and the fact that the air has to flow round the chimney which creates a further complication to the air flow patterns as they mix with the smoke. The mixing of the warm smoke and cooler surrounding air can be likened to the type of turbulent flow which takes place in a thunderstorm or similar local weather disturbance.

You can see further evidence of the turbulent way fluids mix if you watch the flow of water in a river. In the centre of the river you will often get what appears to be a nice, steady flow of water with little turbulence. Towards the banks it is a very different story and here you find that the friction of the water against the fixed banks and the more shallow bottom contours will slow the water down, causing a series of eddies and whirls between this slower moving water and the main stream in the centre of the river. Put an obstruction in the river such as a bridge pier or even a boat and you can immediately see how the smooth water flow is interfered with, creating a sort of vacuum on the lee side of the bridge pier in which the water appears to flow upstream to fill this vacuum. You will be able to see a general pattern to the flow of water in the river as described above, but if you study the flow in detail you will find it is in a constant state of flux, with little whirlpools forming and moving downstream and disappearing with side currents and eddies, and a whole network of what appear at first to be completely random patterns of behaviour. What is happening is that the water is constantly trying to find the state of balance, a level, steady flow, but this sought-after balance is constantly being upset by irregularities in the bottom or the sides of the river. The corrections to try and restore the balance often become overbalanced or over-corrected and interfere with the flow even more, so the state of flux continues. The only time a balanced flow appears to be achieved is when the flow of water in the river is very gentle, which allows time for the irregularities to be corrected before they become obvious.

Rivers of Air

Keep a picture of this river flow in mind when we now try to translate this type of flow pattern into what is happening in the air. The situation in the air is more complicated because the heating of air over the hotter land areas initiates a vertical flow pattern with cold air being sucked in to replace the hot air which is rising. This is what starts off the general patterns of air flow around the world, which results in predictable winds like the trade winds and also most of the less predictable winds, whether local or more widespread. With these main 'rivers' of air we get patterns of turbulence similar to those found in the flow of water in a river. In the trade wind areas where the flow is reasonably steady and predictable, then the turbulence is less than that in the doldrums or along the polar fronts where air flows from different directions intermingle and mix, sometimes creating turbulence which can be particularly violent. On a global scale this turbulence can be seen in temperate latitudes in the form of the major depressions which sweep across the Atlantic and Pacific Oceans in the northern hemisphere, and in the Roaring Forties in the southern hemisphere. These are the major severe weather areas of the world and a major factor in their development is this turbulence created by opposing air streams.

These depressions are somewhat akin to the whirlpools that you can see in a water flow, when faster and slower moving waters intermingle. If you get two water flows running in opposite directions as can occur with

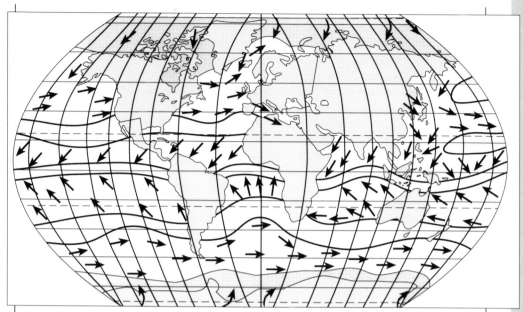

The general wind patterns are affected a great deal by the land masses.

strong tidal streams, then these whirlpools can become quite intense and these are similar to the depressions which sweep along the polar fronts. Whilst you tend to view this turbulence and its effects from a two dimensional viewpoint it is very much a three dimensional phenomenon and occurs at all levels in the atmosphere. Long years of detailed study of these major turbulence factors have enabled meteorologists to predict fairly accurately their track, development and decline. Despite the apparent randomness of this turbulence viewed on a global scale, the forecast maps of these weather patterns can be relied on to a very large degree for periods up to five days ahead.

The problems start for yacht sailors once they appreciate that this turbulence in the atmosphere occurs at every level of scale. The anti-cyclones and depressions can be likened to turbulence on a global scale because of the enormous areas of sea and land which they can encompass. The forecasters can usually cope with this scale of turbulence and also the next level which encompasses the behaviour of frontal systems and secondary depressions. Here the relatively short term nature of these phenomena may not allow their forecasting to be accurate over a five day period, but predictions at this level of scale can usually be relied on for 24 or 48 hours. Where things can be much less easy to forecast is when the turbulence comes down to a local level, and here it is the effect of the flow of air over or round the land which often creates local areas of turbulence. These are more akin to the effects of the water flow in a river when it comes into contact with the bed of the river. The meteorologist could predict these local variations in the wind if he was allowed to make

PREDICTING WINDS

forecasts at such a local level but in most cases it is left to the yacht skippers to make their own local predictions. This can be done if they take the trouble to understand the type of effects and variations in the wind which can be caused by its contact with the land.

When the Air Flow is Broken

It is comparatively easy to see how mountains or high cliffs standing in the path of the wind can affect the air flow and one can to a large degree anticipate the pattern of winds which might result from this. There are more subtle effects found on more gentle coastlines and even trees on a river bank can have a noticeable effect on the wind pattern. At an even more local level there is turbulence which can occur around the mast and rigging of a sailboat or across the superstructure of a powerboat. Those with sailboats will be very interested in the air flow round the mast and the turbulence which will result from this because of the effect it will have on the efficiency of the sails. The same will apply to the rigging, but here we are getting into the realms of the rig and sail designers who seek to optimise its efficiency. This is well outside the realms of weather forecasting but it does serve to demonstrate that turbulence occurs at every level in the air flow. Even those with powerboats are interested in the very local turbulence, because the flow of air over the superstructure of the boat can be the factor which decides whether the exhaust fumes are sucked back on board over the transom, an effect which is similar in many respects to the water flow behind the transom of a yacht, with the water flowing in to reduce the vacuum created by the forward movement of the boat.

Because you can't see the air, it is not always easy to appreciate how the air flows in turbulent conditions, so the analogy of the water flow in a river should be borne in mind because many of the characteristics of fluid flow are common to both air and water. The much lighter density of air will make the effects of turbulence less localised than those often found in a water flow and they seem to take place at a slower pace. For example, depressions seem to move at a very sedate pace bearing in mind the often ferocious winds which can be associated with them.

In trying to appreciate the effects of turbulence, we have to remember that it occurs in four dimensions. This can make life very complicated because we tend to look at it only in the two dimensions of the weather map. Turbulence has a very pronounced vertical aspect as well and you can be very aware of this in the towering clouds of thunderstorms or in areas where there are high cliffs or mountains. This vertical component is the third dimension – and of course the dimension of time is also very important.

Pressure Variations

In trying to predict the wind, the atmospheric or barometric pressure has a vital role to play. A single reading of the barometer will not help you very much because it won't show change. What is much more important is whether there is a difference in the barometer readings either over a period of time in one place or between two adjacent places. This is why meteorologists use synoptic charts for most of their forecasting. Synoptic charts are maps covering a sufficiently large area to show the whole weather pattern in which you are interested, and the basis of much of these synoptic charts is the relative barometric pressure. Pressure is shown on the synoptic charts by isobars which are lines joining places of equal barometric pressure and it is from these isobars that one can build up a picture of where the areas of low pressure (depressions) and the areas of high pressure (anti-cyclones) are.

The Coriolis Force
Rather like water flowing downhill, air tends to flow from areas of high pressure towards areas of low pressure; but like so many things in meteorology, this flow of air is far from simple. There are several other forces acting on this air flow which tend to make it deviate from its logical 'downhill' path, the most significant of these being the Coriolis effect caused by the earth's rotation. Instead of the air flowing directly from the high pressure to the low pressure, it tends to flow in a spiral rather like water draining down a plug hole in the bath. It is the Coriolis effect which is largely responsible for the familiar pattern of winds around high pressures and low pressures, but the rotation of the air around these centres also generates a centrifugal force. Centrifugal force is the familiar effect that anything spinning in a circle tends to get thrown outwards from the centre, so when centrifugal force and the Coriolis force combine, the circular flow of air around both high pressure and low pressure areas tends to follow the lines of the isobars. This explains the value of the synoptic charts for weather forecasting because the lines of isobars also indicate the direction of the wind, usually to within twenty or thirty degrees of what it actually is.

The wind flowing into an area of low pressure tends to be angled slightly inwards from the lines of the isobars towards the centre of the low pressure, whilst the air flowing around an area of high pressure tends to flow slightly outwards from the centre rather than following the direct line of the isobars. This is the predictable wind flow pattern around these major weather features which we have called global turbulence. It is this air flow which is generally used to provide the basis of general weather forecasts because it is relatively easy to predict. Life would be simple if it wasn't for the effects of friction and the smaller scale turbulence which friction generates.

Global Friction
The main effect of friction between the moving air and the earth's surface is that the air close to the surface is slowed down, whilst that higher up moves faster. As we have seen when looking at the behaviour of air flows in general, any difference in speed between adjacent air flows generates turbulence and so when we are looking at the level of the atmosphere in

which yachts operate, which is immediately above the surface, there is almost inevitably a degree of instability in this air flow. This instability will be magnified considerably where there is a line of cliffs in the way of an air flow coming off the sea. In addition, the wind flow over land is always slowed down more than that over the surface of the sea, and this is another cause of turbulence when the wind flows from the sea to the land or vice versa.

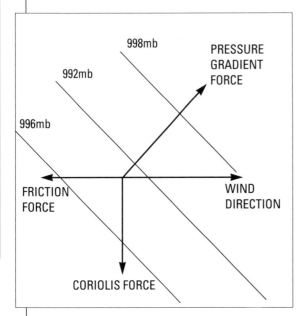

Although the pressure gradient is the primary cause of the wind as it flows from high pressure to low pressure areas at right angles to the isobars, friction and the Coriolis force have a major influence, so that the resulting wind direction is more parallel to the isobars than across them.

The upper winds at 700 metres (2,300 ft) will tend to follow closely the lines of the isobars. At the surface, friction affects the wind direction altering the wind direction by around thirty degrees over the land and perhaps fifteen degrees over the sea.

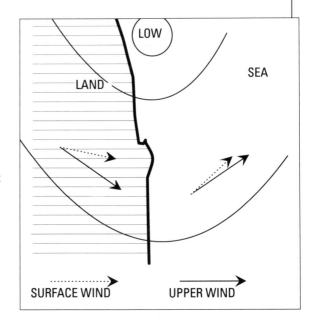

PREDICTING WINDS

In making their assessment of the wind direction and strength, meteorologists will often use as their reference what is called the geostrophic wind, which is the wind speed and direction at a level of 700 metres (2,300ft) above sea level. At this height the wind is generally free of the turbulence generated by contact with the surface of the earth or sea, except of course in mountainous regions, and the wind will follow a more steady pattern which can be related almost directly to the isobars shown on the weather chart. The direction of this geostrophic wind can be determined reasonably accurately from the direction of the isobars and its strength is determined by the distance apart of the isobars. Many weather charts will have a geostrophic wind scale in the corner which shows a series of curves relating to latitude and different wind strengths. By measuring the distance apart of the isobars which cover the area of interest, and relating these to the appropriate geostrophic wind scale at the particular latitude and looking at their direction, it will be possible to get a reasonably accurate estimate of the expected wind strength. Remember this will be the wind strength and direction at 700 metres, and in developing the forecast the meteorologist will then have to correct this in strength and direction to find the winds which can be expected at the sea surface.

In terms of direction, there is likely to be a twenty to thirty degree difference between the wind direction at 700 metres above sea level and that at the surface, with the winds at the surface pointing in more towards the centre of a depression, or out from the centre of an anti-cyclone. The wind direction at 700 metres will conform reasonably accurately with the lines of the isobars. This means that if the wind direction at 700 metres is 090 degrees then at the surface you can expect to find a wind between 060 and 070 degrees. In terms of the strength of the wind, the wind at the surface is likely to be about two thirds of the wind strength found at 700 metres over the sea, whilst the wind strength over the land could be just half of the wind strength at 700 metres because of the increased friction of the wind passing over the land.

Interpreting Isobars
If you are looking at a forecast chart showing isobars, it is important to know what the isobars represent. Many forecast charts show the isobars at 700 metres simply because this is a more reliable and clearer indication of the general wind patterns. Such charts will probably have a geostrophic wind scale inserted alongside them in order to assess the wind strengths and if you have such a chart in front of you then you will have to apply the corrections mentioned above in order to gauge what the surface wind might be. If you have a surface chart showing the forecast isobars at the surface it will probably look very similar in the general pattern, but you will need a different scale to interpret the wind strengths for the surface winds and you will need to make allowance for the fact that the winds at the surface will point in more towards the centre of a depression, or outwards from the centre of an anti-cyclone.

PREDICTING WINDS

Yachts tend to work in or around a particular latitude and therefore instead of the wide-ranging wind scales found on the general weather charts there have been specific wind scales developed which are simpler and easier to use, provided their use is restricted to a specific latitude. These wind scales are available for instance for use with the RYA weather chart format used for interpreting shipping forecasts but it is vitally important if you are using one of these scales to make sure that it is relevant to the scale of the particular weather chart that is in use as well as to the relevant latitude. It also has to be designed for use with the specific isobar scales used on the chart. Most of these scales relate to isobars at 4 mb spacings, but some weather charts have isobars only at 8 mb intervals, which would render the scale at worst useless or at best difficult to use.

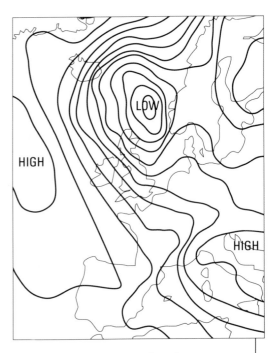

Although isobars on a weather chart are often drawn as evenly spaced lines, this chart demonstrates the sort of local variations which can occur, creating local increases in wind strength where the isobars come close together. Such local variations could increase the wind strength by one or two numbers on the Beaufort scale.

| Latitude | Distance (nautical miles) ------▶ | | | | | | | | | | | | |
	20	25	30	35	40	45	50	60	80	100	150	200	300
10°										133	89	67	44
20°							136	113	85	68	45	34	23
30°				131	115	102	92	77	57	46	31	23	15
40°			119	102	89	80	72	60	45	36	24	18	12
50°		121	101	86	75	67	60	50	38	30	21	15	10
60°	132	105	88	75	66	59	53	44	33	26	18	13	9
70°	122	98	81	70	61	54	49	41	31	24	16	12	8
80°	118	93	79	67	59	52	47	39	29	24	16	12	8
90°	115	92	77	66	57	51	46	38	29	23	15	11	8
	Geostrophic wind speed (knots) ------▶												

By measuring the distance between 4mb isobars on a weather chart it is possible to calculate the expected wind speed. The speeds will also vary with latitude as this chart shows.

The other point to bear in mind when using the distance between isobars to determine wind strength, is that the isobars tend to be drawn in nice, regular consistent lines which would tend to indicate that the wind has a nice regular direction and strength pattern. This can certainly be the case in some conditions of wind over the open sea, but there can always be the risk of local aberrations in the pattern of isobars which are not shown up in the general pattern. For example, a tightening of the isobars in a comparatively small area could push the wind strength up by one or two numbers on the Beaufort Scale and there is some evidence in the case of the 1979 Fastnet storm, that a very small but quite intense secondary low developed which was not evident on the main synoptic chart.

Gusts and Squalls
Such local differences are much more likely to occur in very strong winds when the whole air flow is much more mobile and probably much more turbulent. Local areas of increased wind strength are more likely to be found in the vicinity of fronts, particularly in the vicinity of a cold front where conditions tend to be more intense and localised and where the switch in wind direction as the front passes through can be 90 degrees or more.

Another situation in which local changes of wind strength can occur is when a low pressure area changes direction. It is often noticeable with depressions that there is an area of intense winds in one particular sector of the depression, an area which is identifiable by its closely packed isobars. A change of direction of the depression or even a wobble in its path can lead to a temporary compression of isobars as they appear to adjust to accommodate the new pattern of movement, and it would be reasonable to expect that there could be some form of ripple effect as the

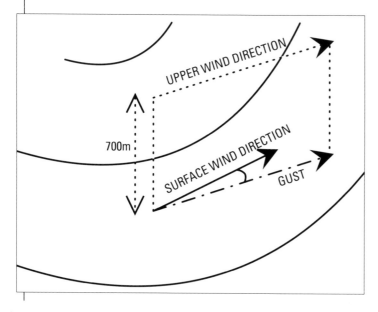

Gusts of wind at the sea surface tend to correspond in direction to the winds at 700 metres (2,300ft). They will be 20 to 30 degrees clockwise of the general surface wind.

isobars strive to even out their pattern and the resulting air flow, creating bands of increased wind strength where the isobars have been compressed. It is not easy to find evidence of these phenomena because they can only be determined by closely spaced comparative measurements which are not available over sea areas and which may not necessarily prove reliable when taken over land areas where the varying effects of friction and land shape can give a false impression. However experience at sea in open sea conditions away from the land does suggest that there can be considerable local variations in wind strength which generally occur in, or at least are particularly noticeable in, more extreme wind conditions. This suggests that there is a greater instability in the pattern of isobars in these conditions than the general weather maps might suggest and that these variations are often more than just gusts of wind. These gusts are a short-lived counterpart of the wide variations of wind strength and, to some extent, direction which can be expected in more extreme conditions.

Gusts are a feature of most strong wind situations and reflect the general instability of the wind, instability generated by the turbulence of the wind in contact with the sea. Everyone with a sailboat will be aware of these gusts which are generally short-lived, usually lasting for only a few minutes but often increasing the wind strength by up to two numbers on the Beaufort Scale. Squalls are a somewhat similar phenomenon but tend to be related more to temperature differences in the air and so to be more prolonged and generally more visible. Squalls are often associated with rain, and it can be the condensing of the water vapour contained in clouds which releases heat, which in turn provides the thermal energy which helps to generate the squall. Whilst not easily predictable in terms of location, squalls can be predictable in a more general way as a result of the prevailing meteorological conditions. We will look at them in more detail

Wind speed range	Factor for maximum gust speed	Factor for mean gust speed	Factor for assessing yacht mean speed
Daytime			
Force 3-4	2.0	1.6	1.8
Force 5-6	1.8	1.5	1.25
Force 7-8	1.6	1.5	1.25
Night-time			
Force 3-4	1.9	1.5	1.5
Force 5-6	1.8	1.5	1.5
Force 7-8	1.7	1.5	1.5

This table provides a means of calculating the maximum winds which can be expected based on forecast values. The forecast value doesn't allow for gusts, whereas the table shows the wind speed can be double the forecast strength. Gusts tend to be less violent at night, hence the reduced correction factors.

in a later chapter on meteorological phenomena, but they are part of a pattern of localised turbulence which can be found even in open sea conditions.

Winds in Coastal Waters

Apart from this type of thermal turbulence, wind conditions out at sea in light or moderate conditions are generally fairly stable and predictable. It is when the wind starts to come into contact with the land or flows from the land over the sea that there can be considerable local variations in the wind patterns from those forecast. Your interpretation of the forecast in relation to local conditions is particularly relevant when sailing near land, in estuaries or narrow channels or in the vicinity of islands. All of these land features will have an effect on the wind. They will generate local turbulence which can affect both wind strength and direction, but in addition there is the temperature difference between sea and land, and there are also other influences, many of which can be very significant not only if you are racing in a sailboat but also if you are reassessing your margin of safety in view of their local effect on sea conditions.

We have already mentioned how friction between the wind and the surface of the sea and land causes the wind direction to change, and that there is a difference in this friction element over the sea and over the land. The reduction in friction as the wind blows from the land on to the sea will not only cause the wind to increase in strength but will also cause it to veer in direction up to thirty degrees as it moves out over the water. The problem here in trying to assess which wind direction you can anticipate is whether the forecast direction is that of the wind over the land or the wind over the sea.

In general you can anticipate that it is the wind over the sea which is the forecast direction and therefore this veering of the wind as it hits the water is not likely to create any nasty surprises for yachts at sea. However, if you are trying to sail up towards a harbour entrance close hauled on the starboard tack, then you could find that the wind is coming ahead just at the time when you thought you had a good, fair wind all the way into the harbour entrance. This is because the wind appears to veer as you approach land.

Cliffs

Another point to consider when the wind is blowing from the land out to sea at a near right angle is that you can often find an area of calm or even reverse winds close inshore. This is going to be particularly the case when there are high cliffs and these areas of calm or reverse winds are simply a turbulence eddy set up as the wind tries to fill the partial vacuum which develops in the lee of the cliff, rather like the effect of water behind a bridge pier. Close inshore, that is up to half a mile from the land, you can get a pronounced eddy wind flowing in the opposite direction, particularly if the wind coming over the cliff is quite strong. These eddies can be found up to four miles offshore in strong winds and in relation to high cliffs. The wind in this area is not likely to be very consistent in any wind strength and you could find quite strong winds interspersed with areas of comparative calm. In light winds these eddies under the cliffs will be virtually non-existent. In stronger winds there could be considerable gusting and turbulence and this can be quite disconcerting when you think that you are approaching a weather shore and then find that you end up approaching what appears to be a lee shore with the wind blowing you on to the land.

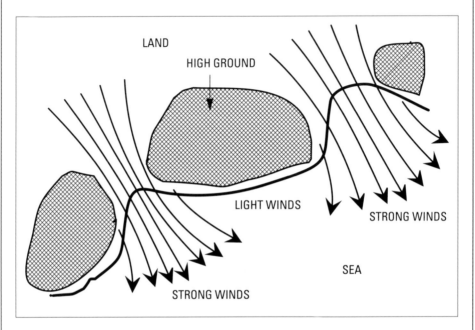

How wind can be funnelled down river valleys as it approaches the sea. This effect can create locally strong winds with lighter winds in the shelter of higher ground.

In some air conditions you may find evidence of this phenomenon in the form of clouds lying just off the coast. You have to remember that this turbulence is three dimensional and the main air stream flowing off the edge of the cliff can set up a series of waves with the eddies forming underneath them. It is in the crest of these wind waves that you may find clouds which indicate where the air sweeping upwards towards the crest is meeting the more stable air flow directly off the land above the cliff. A great deal depends on the height of the cliff and the strength of the wind and the main thing when you are in the lee of cliffs in this way is to be aware of the uncertainty of the wind strength and direction rather than to expect to find any fixed pattern.

Lines of cliff in this situation are rarely long and regular in height, and they are often interspersed by deep valleys. These steep sided valleys can tend to concentrate the wind flow off the land and here you will be likely to find a stronger wind because of the funnelling effect, but without the eddies found in the lee of a cliff. There is also a gradient effect created by the slope of the valley which tends to accelerate the wind speed, so you can expect to find local winds here considerably in excess of those in the lee of the adjacent cliffs. Whilst the main flow out of such a valley can be quite strong and consistent, at the edge of this flow there will be considerable turbulence and eddies because of the variation in speed of the different air masses. These are the sort of conditions where you can find quite violent squalls building up as a sort of vortex which sweeps down the mountain valley. You can often see these sweeping towards you as an area of white water on the sea surface generated by the intense wind energy. Such violent squalls are a feature of mountainous areas where there are steep mountains interspersed by steep sided valleys. Because the sea areas involved are generally sheltered from the prevailing wind, these squalls are not particularly dangerous in terms of the sea conditions they generate, but there is danger in the very fierce winds which can be found and their highly variable direction. It is not unknown for a wind to swing right round through 360 degrees in a matter of minutes, and this highly variable direction combined with the intense wind strength can make life very difficult for a sailboat whether under way or at anchor.

Islands

The same sort of turbulent conditions will often be found in the lee of islands in strong wind conditions. An island acts rather like the bridge pier in the middle of a river upsetting the flow of the water which has to come round each side of the pier. With an island the flow is even more confused because not only does the wind come round each side of the island, but it also comes over the top. Much will depend on the topography of the island itself as well as the direction of the wind, and obviously a high peaked island will provide greater intrusion into the main air stream than a low, flat island. With most islands the air stream flowing over the land of the island is slowed down, whilst the main air flow passing each side of the island will often change direction by 10 or 15 degrees as it swerves to accommodate the island. This change of direction is more likely to be noticeable in the lee of an island as the air moves in to fill the partial vacuum created by the island itself. It is easy to see that there could be considerable turbulence in the lee of an island with eddies and vortexes forming, particularly in strong winds, and with larger steep sided islands this turbulence can extend for many miles down wind.

Regional Winds

Whilst we have been looking at comparatively local effects here, where the wind runs off the land and around small islands, these effects can be seen on a much wider scale, particularly in some regions of the Mediterranean. Here the high mountains of the Alps can form a barrier between the relatively cold air to the north and the warm air to the south. There are significant local winds in these regions which are generally formed by a cold front building up air against the north slope of the Alps which effectively blocks any further movement of this cold air south. Eventually this cold air looks for a way out because the imbalance between it and the warmer air to the south becomes stronger, and the air filters out in a very strong air flow down the main valleys which run through gaps in the mountains. The air flow down the Rhone Valley is one of the most famous, and this creates the local wind called the Mistral. Once set in motion this wind can last for several days as the cold air runs its course south. It can generate winds of gale force out over the adjacent sea areas of the Mediterranean.

There are similar winds towards the eastern end of the Alps called the Bora and the Tramontana, both of which carry cold winds from the north into the Adriatic Sea. These winds, although created by different means from some of the more local winds found on coastlines, show many of the characteristics of wind coming off the land. They can generate a wide variety of turbulence effects as they pass from the land to the sea. It is important to remember that what might look a nice comfortable, sheltered coastline as you approach it from seaward can hide some nasty surprises in terms of local winds and turbulence. As far as a powerboat is concerned there should not be too much problem because the fetch is small, but with a sailboat, some of this turbulence can be quite vicious and can catch you unawares.

Winds Parallel to the Shore
There are situations where the strength of the wind blowing parallel or nearly parallel to the coastline can vary considerably. Even when the shore line is quite low, the wind direction will tend to follow the coastline even though its general course as predicted on the forecast may be twenty or thirty degrees different from the line of the coast. The wind apparently prefers the easier path over the water than the more turbulent path over the land and bends its direction accordingly. With more pronounced coastlines where there are cliffs or high ground adjacent to the water, then the effect on the wind is more pronounced.

Wind direction might still be fairly easy to anticipate if coastlines followed regular lines and were even, but this is rarely the case and the irregular nature of the coastline can create local turbulence. As the wind blows along cliff edges it can be slowed down considerably in comparison with the main flow of air further offshore. This local turbulence is similar in many respects to that found when the wind blows around islands and whilst the main body of the wind is slowed, the turbulence generated can be responsible for the gusty conditions which can often be found within a few miles of the land, when the wind is blowing along the coastline.

More pronounced and potentially more dangerous is the effect on this wind flow when it meets significant headlands. A pronounced headland which juts out into the air flow effectively causes the air to be funnelled through a narrower gap. This means that its velocity increases which explains why you often find considerably stronger winds around a headland. The effect is much the same as that found with strong tides or currents and if you look at the tidal atlas, you will see that in the English Channel for instance, there is always a stronger tide around each headland which sticks out into the tidal flow. Although you can't see it the same thing can occur with the wind, and with a westerly or south westerly wind blowing up the English Channel you will always find stronger winds, probably one or two numbers up in the Beaufort Scale, around the significant headlands, when compared with the general forecast strength of the wind. These local stronger winds around headlands can be particularly dangerous when they are seen in relation to the stronger tidal streams which also flow around these headlands and the combination can generate very dangerous sea conditions. The effect of this strengthening of the wind around headlands will vary considerably depending on the height and prominence of the headland and the wind direction, but wind strengths ten or fifteen knots in excess of the general air flow can be anticipated in strong wind conditions. In addition turbulence can be anticipated in the lee of these pronounced headlands. This is somewhat similar to that found in the lee of islands and is generated by the disturbance of the air flow as some passes over the headland and some passes round it. The resulting turbulent area can extend several miles in the lee of the headland.

Another factor to bear in mind when the wind is blowing along the coastline is that there can be considerable variations in strength and direction of the wind owing to either convergence or divergence. We have

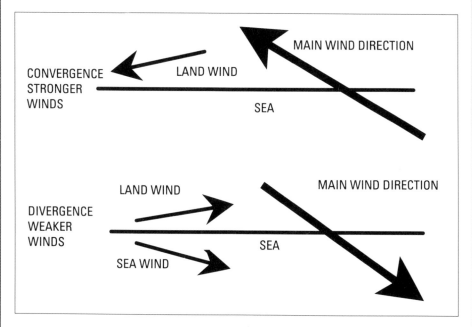

Showing how divergence and convergence of the winds along the coastline can increase or decrease the wind speed. If your back is to the wind, and the land is on your right side, then expect stronger winds. With the land on your left, expect weaker winds.

already seen how a wind blowing off the shore will veer in direction maybe 20 or 30 degrees when it passes from land to water. With the main air flow blowing parallel or nearly parallel to the coastline there will be different angles of the surface wind over the land and water. If you have your back to the wind and the coast is on your right hand side, then the land and sea winds will converge and this will generate a stronger flow of wind along the coastline, increasing the general wind strength perhaps by as much as a quarter. This is a comparatively local effect and may be felt no more than three or four miles off the coastline. It can often be identified by an increase in cloud along the line of the convergence because the air from the convergent air streams is forced upwards to a certain extent.

The reverse occurs when you have the wind on your back and the coastline is on your left hand side. Now the land wind and the sea wind diverge, creating a lighter wind along the shore line and a reduced amount of cloud. These effects of convergence and divergence will often be mistaken for land and sea breeze effects, but they are different and this difference can be identified by the fact that the phenomenon persists both day and night, unlike land or sea breezes.

Sea Breezes

Land and sea breezes are one of the best recognised phenomena occurring near the coastline. Of the two the sea breeze is probably the more significant mainly because it occurs during the daytime and often in calm or light wind conditions when it can provide a good sailing breeze where none has existed before. The catalyst for generating a sea breeze is an imbalance in temperature between the sea and the land and this almost invariably occurs when the land heats up more quickly than the sea under the influence of the morning sun. The higher temperature of the air over the land means that the air here will rise and this in turn sucks in the cooler air to replace it which leaves a partial vacuum over the sea. The rising air over the land is cooled as it rises, heads out seaward at a higher elevation and then drops down over the sea – a circular air flow is thus set up of which the main component as far as yachts are concerned is the sea breeze element flowing from the sea towards the land at sea level.

The sea breeze will start up as a gentle drift of air if the ambient conditions are calm. It will start a little way offshore and then gradually increase and extend seaward. Because of the Coriolis effect the direction of the breeze will gradually turn to the right in the northern hemisphere, whichever way the coast is facing, and the strength of the breeze will steadily increase. When fully formed, which is usually by mid-afternoon, the sea breeze will extend up to ten miles seaward and can be up to Force 3 or 4 in strength, while the direction may have veered 40 to 60 degrees from the initial line of right angles to the coast owing to the Coriolis effect.

So far we have considered the formation of a sea breeze from relatively calm conditions. If there is already a wind blowing then the development of a sea breeze is highly dependent on whether the main air flow is blowing offshore and can form part of the critical element of the circular air flow of

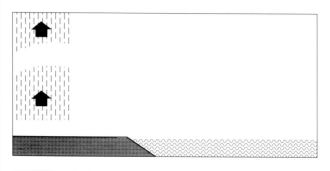

Sea breezes start with the land being heated and the air rising.

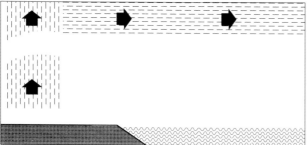

This risng air cools as it rises and flows out to sea.

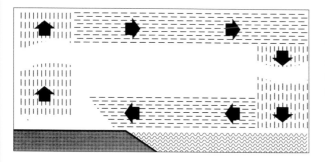

The sea breeze circulation is completed with cooler air flowing in from seaward.

the sea breeze which is the upper section blowing from land to sea. If the main air flow is from land to sea then the chances of the sea breeze developing are minimal. With an offshore air flow, the development of the sea breeze may be preceded by a calm period during which a balance between the sea breeze and the main air flow is established and then the sea breeze can take precedence at sea level allowing the main air flow to maintain its circulation at higher level. With the type of air flow associated with the sea breeze operating in conjunction with the main air flow blowing offshore, there will tend to be a calm patch at the point where the sea breeze air flow circulates over the sea. This means that if you want to get the benefit of the sea breeze for sailing then you need to stay reasonably close inshore. In some more complex situations there can be two calm patches, one further out to sea and one close inshore.

The situation with the sea breeze is complicated not only by the direction of the main air flow but also by the topography of the coastline, and understanding and making use of sea breezes is one of the vital techniques for the racing sailor. For the cruising yacht sea breezes present no hazards in terms of strong winds and with an onshore main air flow the sea breeze tends to strengthen and produce a better sailing wind, whereas with an offshore main air flow, you can expect to find an element of turbulence and possible calms inshore and the best bet is to keep offshore as far as is reasonably possible in order to keep a more stable air flow.

Land and sea breezes are not the only winds which can occur close inshore. Anabatic and katabatic winds have somewhat similar characteristics, but are winds associated with hill slopes. When you get high hills or mountains along the coast, the slope higher up the hill may be heated more by the sun, so that the air above it becomes warmer than the air at a lower level. The warmer air rises and there is a tendency then for the air to be drawn up the slope. Such a wind is called an anabatic wind. The reverse effect, when cold air from higher up tends to flow down the hill to replace warmer air which has risen from lower slopes, is called a katabatic wind. Because the downhill flow is helped by gravity, this katabatic wind is likely to be stronger. Neither of these winds is likely to be felt much out at sea except that the katabatic wind can become accelerated owing to the funnel effect of a mountain valley. This tends to accelerate the air flow, and such a flow could extend out to sea.

How Coastal Winds Affect You

We have looked at the different types of coastal wind independently, but of course two or more can be found in conjunction and it is not always easy to anticipate the final result. If you are looking to gain every advantage from the wind because you are racing then it pays to make a much deeper study of these effects, and local knowledge of winds in a particular region can be a tremendous advantage in racing. Here we are tending to look at the more general effects so that you can gauge the wind direction and strength when you go out for a day's sailing or when you are on a longer cruise. It is not too difficult to imagine what happens when you have an island or headland in the way of the main air flow, and to picture the areas where the wind will be concentrated, where the wind strength is likely to increase around these headlands and around islands. In moderate conditions the local increases in wind strength and the variations in direction are not likely to have any significant effect on the safety of your boating operations and sailboat skippers will probably be more concerned with any changes in direction of the wind rather than in the strength.

However it is when the weather forecast starts to give wind strengths of Force 5 or 6 that you need to become much more aware of the local changes which can occur along coastlines and in enclosed or semi-enclosed waters. This is where the local increases in wind strength can produce winds of gale force and start to create the sort of conditions where you wish you hadn't gone out to sea or you want to start seeking shelter. Local variations in wind strength can be very significant in these conditions, and if you understand what is going on, you will be much better prepared to cope.

Tides and Currents

One final aspect of the wind and the conditions which can affect its strength is the effect of tides and currents. When a body of water is moving, the water will drag the air close to the surface along with it. Tides can be quite strong, often running up to three or four knots locally, and this can have a significant impact on the wind strength, either slowing the wind down if the wind is against the tide, or speeding up the wind if wind and tide are together. This latter effect won't make any difference to your sailing because the tide is also carrying the boat along, and so the relative wind will still be the same as if you were in still water. This certainly applies at sea level, but the height at which the drag effect of the tide extends upwards is not always easy to determine, although it is probably quite low. This means that you could find a situation where there is wind sheer, with the air close to the surface running at one speed, where it is increased or decreased by the tidal flow, and the air perhaps 30 feet above the surface, which could be just half way up the mast, flowing at a different speed which relates to the general wind situation where it is not influenced by the tide. This is a situation which racing boats could exploit, though the main effect which is likely to be noticed by a cruising sailboat is an increase in the turbulence of the air when operating in strong tidal areas which can lead to the wind being more gusty and varying slightly in both direction and strength.

With ocean currents the situation is somewhat different because it is the winds themselves which tend to generate the ocean currents, imparting their energy to the surface of the water and dragging this along to generate the current. This is similar to the frictional effect of the wind on the surface of the sea which has a slowing effect whether or not a current is produced as a result. As ocean currents generally do not exceed one knot in strength, the effects of this situation will be barely noticeable although the effects on sea conditions can be quite significant as we will see in the next chapter.

Wind Forecasts

Predicting winds is quite a complex subject and there are many variables to be taken into account. Fortunately as a yachtsman you rarely have to start from first principles and work out what the wind is going to do without access to weather forecasts. If you should find yourself in this predicament then you will need to keep a regular log of the weather conditions, say every two hours, recording wind strength and direction, cloud cover and type, temperature and barometer readings. From this you should be able to build up a picture of what the weather pattern is doing and the barometer readings will give you an indication of any significant changes. It is these changes with which you are particularly concerned because you know what the weather is at the present time, and presumably you are reasonably comfortable with it, but changes in both wind strength and direction will affect your future tactics. The barometer is your main instrument to sense these changes and we will be looking in a later chapter about how to read local weather signs and develop your own forecasts. In this chapter on predicting the winds we are working primarily on the assumption that you have an adequate forecast of the wind which will form the basis of your predictions.

The basic weather forecast will give both wind strength and direction and there is little cause to argue with what the forecaster is suggesting, but you also need to know when a front will be passing your position, heralding a veer in the wind and perhaps a change in strength. You can get this information to a certain extent from local observation, noting the cloud changes which herald the advance of a front or its passing, but it has to be said that by the time you see the signs of the front the changes are probably imminent. With a weather map obtained from a weatherfax you are much more in control of the situation. The direction and spacing of the isobars will give you a picture of the whole weather situation and if you use the method of plotting advancing fronts and the movements of low pressure areas as suggested in Chapter 3 then you will find that you are able to predict with a high degree of accuracy wind changes likely to affect you. Having a weather chart can give you a great deal of confidence, feeling that you are fully aware of the weather situation and able to predict the winds, but in making these predictions you have to bear in mind all the local variations which can affect the forecast winds.

These local variations are much more likely to occur in coastal waters. However even out in the open sea the carefully drawn and smoothed out lines of the isobars do not always guarantee the steady winds which they suggest. Although it is difficult to find precise evidence because of the restricted number of weather reports out in the open sea, experience suggests that in reality these isobars can be much more wavy and have local aberrations, which can create locally stronger or lighter winds which the general weather forecasts tend to ignore. You can expect to find these gusting winds in the area around a cold front, but evidence from the Fastnet storm suggests that when there are closely packed isobars, the wind arranges itself in corridors of stronger wind interspersed with areas of lighter winds and these stronger winds can be twenty knots or more higher in speed than the average wind speed. It is a situation rather like waves at sea where we talk about average wave heights or significant wave heights, but nonetheless there can be some waves at least twice that height. It seems that the same situation can occur with the wind, but again the evidence of the Fastnet gale suggests that some of these higher force winds can be much more persistent than is normally the case for gusts.

So in trying to predict the wind from a weather chart, or from a weather forecast for that matter, always bear in mind that the wind could be stronger or lighter than the forecast suggests. In terms of the Beaufort Scale this could be two numbers higher or lower than the mean which the forecast gives, and you need to be prepared for these variations. Even larger differences are possible, but in general the greater the difference from the forecast wind, the shorter its duration. Short duration changes in wind strength are unlikely to have much effect on the sea conditions which are potentially more of a risk than the strong winds themselves. Out in the open sea where yachts have to be prepared to cope with the worst, these variations from the forecast winds should not present too much difficulty.

Inshore the situation can be different. Here not only can the funnelling effect of the wind around headlands and through channels have a significant effect on the strength of the wind, it can also have a significant effect on sea conditions particularly when there is wind against tide. Think of the wind as a fluid, and compare it with water being squeezed through narrow channels where its speed increases or where its direction can be diverted. This is how wind will behave in areas where high coastlines can force the wind away from its forecast route. Any change in direction will tend to vary the wind strength, increasing it around headlands or in areas where the wind is compressed into smaller openings. Unlike water the wind can always escape upwards, but any interference with the free passage of the wind will generate turbulence which in itself can increase the strength of the wind and vary its direction. When the wind is strong, the effects of any interference with its passage will be more pronounced. However if in your mind you can see how the friction between the fixed land and the moving air will slow down the air, how compressing the air flow will accelerate its passage, and how changes in temperature can introduce secondary air flow, as in land or sea breezes, then you will start to get a feel for the wind and the way it behaves. No amount of bland weather charts or forecasts can generate this instinctive understanding which is the key to forecasting the wind.

At the end of the day it is this feel, this emotional involvement with the wind which will allow you to predict its behaviour and will take away some of the nasty surprises which seem to catch out yacht skippers who fail to realise the changes taking place.

PREDICTING WINDS

6 Wind and Sea State

The wind is obviously of importance to those using sails for propulsion but the sea conditions generated by the wind are important to everyone who goes to sea, not just because the waves affect the level of comfort on board but also because it is the waves which create much of the danger and risk at sea. In addition waves can directly affect the performance of a powerboat and have a significant effect on the level of stresses and strains on a sailboat.

Waves come in a wide variety of shapes and sizes and it is often the shape rather than the size which is important. It is the steep waves with breaking crests which can create a very real danger to small craft. For the powerboat skipper, waves are critical to performance and comfort – unlike the sailboat, where it is the wind which largely dictates the speed, a powerboat's performance is limited by the waves. The size and shape of waves are very much related to wind strength, so whilst the waves are not directly a part of the weather pattern they should be a part of your personalised weather forecast.

Wind and Waves

The wind affects the surface of the water over which it blows in a variety of ways. It is the wind which is largely responsible for generating ocean surface currents, dragging the surface water along by friction. It is the wind which is responsible for generating the waves on the surface of the sea and again the friction link is partly responsible for this. Although the two fluids involved have very different characteristics, the interaction between them creates turbulence just as it does when air masses mix, making the sea one of the more unpredictable areas on the surface of the earth for which to try to forecast the weather.

The wind is not the only influence on waves in this inhospitable region. Tides, currents, land masses, rocks, shallow water and even passing ships have to be taken into account when trying to assess what size and shape of waves will be generated. Just as it is possible to get a broad picture of what the wind regime will be like from the forecasts, a general indication of wave patterns and trends can also be derived from forecasts. However there will also be a variety of local influences which can affect the size and shape of the waves and the element of danger which they can present to

An estimated 8 metre high wave becoming unstable and starting to break. Although the near vertical wave front looks frightening, once the top of the crest has broken, the wave stabilises and does not break over the full height of the wave.

yachts. Just like the wind forecasts, any general forecast of wave heights and direction has to be fine-tuned in order to take account of local conditions. Waves are a very complex subject and one which is still not fully understood, but the yacht skipper can do a great deal to interpret and improve the forecast.

Two Fluids: Air and Water

The surface of the sea is the meeting point between two fluids, the air and the water. We have seen in our study of winds how, when two fluids are moving in relation to each other, an area of turbulence is set up. Few yacht skippers are going to disagree when we describe the meeting of air and water as an area of turbulence, particularly when the wind is blowing strongly. Even out in the open sea away from the complicating effects of tides, land and shallow water, the surface of the sea still presents a turbulent picture to the yachtsman. Whilst the waves represent the visible evidence of this turbulence on the surface of the water, you can assume that there is an equal amount of turbulence in the air above, although of course you can't see this directly. This interface between air and water can generate very hostile conditions and it is a measure of modern yacht design that small craft can not only survive in this turbulent area but can also make progress.

Just imagine that we have still water and still air. In this condition there will be no interaction between air and water, but once the air starts to move we find interaction between the two fluids starting and this has two results. Firstly the air starts to drag the surface water along with it, because of the friction effect between the air and the water. This sets up currents in the water, which we will look at later, but it also generates turbulence in the air. This very local turbulence may be on quite a small scale, but it is the creation of small areas of low and high pressure within this air turbulence which affects the water surface and makes this uneven, so that ripples start to form. Once these ripples start to form then they increase the irregularity of the surface and this in turn will tend to increase the friction and the turbulence of the air.

If we now assume that there is a steady horizontal air flow over the water surface, then this air flow will exert a greater force on the windward slope of the ripples than on the leeward side. This causes the ripples to be driven along in the direction of the wind and as long as the wind is moving more rapidly than the waves it is generating, then the waves will tend to increase in size.

These initial ripples are one of the five different types of waves which you can encounter at sea, and it is quite important to understand these different types because they will have different effects on the behaviour of the waves, which in turn will affect your yacht. To know how they affect the performance and safety of yachts you need to know how and when they are likely to be formed.

Five Types of Waves
The five types of waves are ripples, oscillation waves, pressure waves, translation waves and the delightfully named clapotic waves. Apart from pressure waves, all of these are primarily generated by the wind, but some change type after they have come into contact with other features such as shallow water, tidal streams or currents, and the land itself. It is the way in which waves are modified by these other influences, together with the combination of different types of waves, which can produce some of the more dangerous and unpredictable seas to be found in rough weather.

Ripples and Oscillation Waves
Waves start off as ripples which are formed in very light wind conditions, but these soon grow into small wavelets as the wind strength increases. These wavelets then grow into recognisable waves. In an ideal wave form, all the water particles within that wave revolve at the same speed in a circular orbit, which is perpendicular to the crest of the wave. You can see this if you watch waves in a harbour where there is some light debris lying

on the water surface. The debris will tend to bob backwards and forwards and up and down as the waves pass and in fact the debris is following part of the circular motion of the water particles, although being buoyant the debris doesn't complete the full circle made by the water particles in the waves. At the crest of the wave the motion of the water particles is horizontal in the direction of the wind, and they also move horizontally in the trough but in the opposite direction to the crest. This circular motion, with the water particles not making any positive forward progress under the influence of the wind, represents the ideal wave and the influence of this water movement is confined to the body of water relatively close to the surface. At a depth equivalent to one wave length, which is the distance between one wave crest and the next, the movement of the water particles relating to the wave is virtually damped out so that the water at this one wave length depth is largely undisturbed.

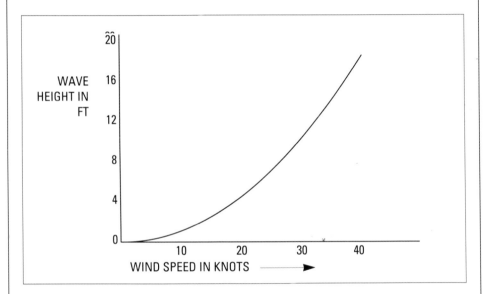

The height of waves in relation to various wind speeds. These are the average wave heights you might expect to find in open waters.

Waves formed in this way under the influence of the wind are called oscillation waves because the water tends to oscillate. These are the common form of wave which you find in the open sea and they are created from the energy imparted by the wind. There is a direct relationship between the wind strength and the wave height. Under the influence of the wind the waves will continue to build up until a state of equilibrium is reached. It is easy to visualise that an oscillation wave has to be supported by a certain amount of energy from the wind otherwise it would simply collapse and the sea surface would become flat again. It is the pressure of the wind on the windward side of the wave which supplies the energy to support the waves but the energy required is quite small, because although the waves give the appearance that the mass of water is moving bodily forwards, the circular rotation of the particles within the wave indicates that the water is virtually static within the moving wave trains, and the water particles rise and fall as the waves pass a fixed point but do not move bodily forward.

In theory, once a wave train has been started by the action of the wind, it would keep going forever if it were not for the internal friction created by the movement of the water particles and the surface tension of the water, both of which act gradually to slow down the waves after the wind has stopped imparting energy to them. These residual waves which are not wind supported are what we call swell, and the fact that wave trains can persist in the form of swell for a considerable period after the wind has changed or dropped, is one of the factors which complicates the forecasting of wave heights and directions and which can also contribute to the formation of freak waves.

In theory the shape of an oscillation wave should follow the tidy pattern of a sine curve. The waves generated by the wind should produce a regular series of waves of similar height and shape. In practice however waves will vary considerably in height and shape. The wind itself modifies the shape of the wave simply because it is exerting pressure on one side of the wave and there is a semi-vacuum on the other side in the lee of the wind. This means that the wave is likely to be more convex on the windward side and more concave on the leeward side, particularly near the top of the wave where the influence of the wind is greater. This change in the shape of the wave can become more extreme as the wind strength increases.

Translation Waves
This brings us to translation waves which is the technical name for waves that are breaking. Sailors have always had a fear of breaking waves because with this type the top of the wave has become unstable and started to gain its own momentum and rush forward under the influence of the wind. Instead of having a body of water where the particles are moving round in relatively harmless circles with virtually no inherent momentum, the particles in translation waves change into a moving body of water which has a significant amount of force and momentum, which can provide a frightening picture to the sailor on a small boat. These breaking waves are called translation waves because the latent energy in the waves is translated into forward motion.

The best example of translation waves is probably waves breaking on a beach. Here the instability in the wave is caused by the bottom of the wave being slowed down as it comes into contact with the sea bed. The top of the wave is still travelling forward at its original speed, and the initial effect of this slowing down of the wave is to reduce the wave length. You can see this if you watch waves approaching the shore where you will notice that the wave crests will move closer together as the wave length shortens, because the wave is being slowed down. This shortening of the wave length will increase the gradient of the waves and eventually the wave becomes unstable and breaks.

In shallow waters such as a beach or sandbank, these translation waves will become unstable and break in a very different manner to that found in the open sea. At sea, the crest of the wave very rarely rears up and crashes forward in a big welter of foam, but rather the crest of the wave tends to run down the face of the wave in a more gradual process. This is because it is only wind pressure which is causing the instability of the wave and this has a greater effect near the crest so that the instability tends to be restricted to this part of the wave. After the initial breaking of the crest, the wave tends to return to a stable form whilst still moving ahead at the same pace. In shallow water, because of the slowing down of the wave by the sea bed, the wave tends to trip over itself. A near vertical wall of water is formed before the crest falls violently into the trough, and the energy of the wave is translated into horizontal energy with the water flowing strongly forward.

The waves on a bar get shorter and steeper and can become breaking (translation) waves as the water shoals. The conditions can become dangerous when an onshore wind meets an outgoing tide.

You can get these same violent breaking crests at sea but they usually occur in extreme conditions, and even then they are more likely to be the result of two wave crests coinciding suddenly to produce the same sort of major instability as we see in the breaking waves on the beach. Translation waves are almost invariably the result of instability where the wave length has shortened or where the wave has grown in height and the gradient or angle of the wave slope has steepened.

Wave Length and Height

It is worth looking here at this relationship between gradient and wave length and height, because these are the critical factors which affect waves and the boats which are operating in them. The wave length is the distance from the crest of one wave to the crest of the next wave. Wave height is the height from the bottom of the trough between two crests to the top of the crest. The period of waves is the time it takes for two successive wave crests to pass a fixed point, and the gradient is the angle of the wave slope to the horizontal. There are close relationships between some of these factors affecting wave shape and size.

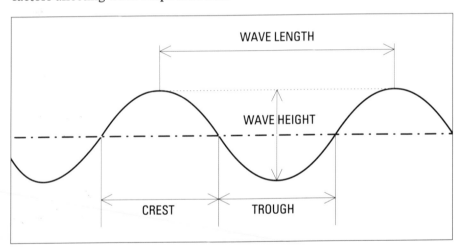

Some of the terms used when talking about waves.

The wave length when measured in metres is equal to 1.56 times the wave period when measured in seconds. The speed of a wave measured in knots is equal to 3.1 times the period measured in seconds, and what this means in practice is that the larger or higher the wave, the faster it will travel. This is because wave length is in turn directly related to wave height and so the greater the wave length the faster the wave will travel. For instance the typical 25 metre wave length, which might be found in coastal waters in a moderate breeze, will result in waves travelling at just over 12 knots. Out in the open sea, where the wave length might be longer, say 156 metres, then the waves will be travelling at 31 knots. Ocean swells of very long wave length can travel at speeds of several hundred knots which sounds frightening, but the very low height of these waves will make them barely perceptible. The main relevance of wave speeds comes when you are operating in following seas where the speed at which the wave is overtaking you can determine how you cope with it. In a planing powerboat it is possible to overtake waves, whilst in some sailboats it is possible to plane down the front of a wave. The speed of waves can be affected by external influences such as tides and shallow water which can lengthen or shorten the wave length.

Wave Gradients

An important factor in describing waves and one which is particularly relevant to yachts is the gradient. Although your experience with waves at sea might suggest otherwise, most waves have a very gentle gradient probably in the region of only 10 or 15 degrees from the horizontal. When you are pitching into a head sea, you may think that the gradient of the waves feels a lot steeper than this, but you have to remember that here we are talking about the average gradient of the waves and the theoretical shape of waves following a sine curve. A real wave at sea will tend to have a steeper gradient near its crest on the lee side because of the pressure of the wind from the other side creating the concave shape. What you feel and see in practice tends to be the steeper part of the wave, rather than the average gradient and this steeper part could have a gradient of fifteen to eighteen degrees.

It is a combination of the wave height and the wave length which determines the gradient. A 6 metre wave with a wave length of 300 metres will have a very gentle gradient even though the waves are quite high. Such a wave would more likely be construed as a swell and a more common wave length for this height of wave would be 70 to 90 metres in the open ocean which certainly produces a steeper and more dangerous gradient. It is generally reckoned that a critical gradient for a wave is 18 degrees because with anything steeper than this gradient the wave can no longer support its own weight through the wind pressure and it will tend to become unstable. At this point there is a risk that the crest will start to curl over and break to leeward in response to the instability.

White Horses

There are two main causes for waves getting into this unstable situation and becoming translation waves. One is the pressure of the wind itself acting on the wave and the other is external influences such as shallow water, tides and the land. The waves obviously cannot travel as fast as the wind which creates them, and the speed differential between the wind and the waves increases as the wind speed rises. As the wind is exerting pressure on the windward side of the wave there is an eddy or low pressure area on the lee side which tends to increase as the size of the wave grows. The pressure exerted by the wind increases towards the top of the wave and the low pressure area or eddy is likely to be more intense near the top, particularly if this wave is higher than the average of the wave train of which it is part and thus more exposed to the influence of the wind. This increase in pressure towards the top of the wave means that the top of the wave wants to move faster to leeward than the bottom of the wave. This creates a situation of instability and increases the gradient on the lee side, causing the top of the wave to break to leeward in order to try and restore stability. This type of breaking of the wave crest tends to occur at the first signs of instability and is the main cause of 'white horses' which are to be found when the wind strength exceeds Force 4.

These 'white horses' are not particularly dangerous for yachts as it is only the very top of the wave which breaks to leeward and there is not very much strength or volume in the breaking water. This comparatively minor breaking of the crest temporarily relieves the pressure differences around the wave and it quickly stabilises again. It is only when winds start to exceed Force 8 that the 'white horses' can become significant and dangerous. At this wind strength the waves in general start to take on a new shape and significance and the breaking of the crests can become more intense and dangerous because there is considerably more weight and volume there. At these higher wind strengths the instability caused by the increase in gradient means that the 'white horses' tend to lose their random character and become a much more regular occurrence.

As soon as the wind decreases the 'white horses' disappear, although the waves remain, demonstrating that these are primarily a wind generated phenomenon. At moderate wind strengths, the amount of water actually in motion as the wave breaks in 'white horses' is small and will present little hazard to a small boat, but as the wind strength increases the volume and depth of the breaking water increases so that in severe conditions these breaking wave crests could easily overwhelm the boat.

Waves in Shallow Water
Thus it is only in very strong winds that the wind generated instability becomes serious and the translation waves become significant. However there are other factors which can affect the gradient of the wave and thus convert oscillation waves into translation waves and which can create dangerous areas for yachts. An obvious area here as we have already seen will be when waves are breaking on to a beach. Because the wave is slowed down as it approaches the beach, the wave length becomes shorter and the gradient increases leading to the instability which causes the wave to break over a long front and crash down on to the beach. This is not an area where yachts would be operating from choice, but you can get similar effects over shoals, even though these don't dry out. What might be a perfectly acceptable stretch of shallow water to cross in calm or moderate conditions could produce dangerous breaking sea conditions when there are larger waves.

The cause of a wave breaking in shallow water is that the bottom of the wave, which can extend some depth below the surface, is slowed down by its proximity to the sea bed. The top of the wave is still travelling forwards at its original speed and the slowing down process results in a reduction in the wave length which in turn increases the gradient and eventually the wave becomes unstable and breaks. In shoal water a wave tends to break in a very different manner from that in which it breaks in the open sea. In the open sea the crest tends to run down the face of a wave in a relatively gradual process. In shallow water because of the slowing of the bottom of the wave by the sea bed, the wave tends to trip over itself and a near vertical wall of water is formed before the crest falls violently into the trough and the energy of the waves is translated into a strong, horizontal flow of water.

In shallow water it is the depth of the water and the size of the waves which are the critical factors in deciding whether waves break or not. Even if the waves don't break you may still be able to feel the influence of the shallow water by a discernible shortening of the wave length and an apparent steepening of the gradient, which in combination with other factors can generate quite nasty sea conditions.

Shoaling Shortens the Wave Length

The depth of water at which a wave will start to slow and shorten its wave length is roughly equal to the wave length itself. A typical wave length for waves in inshore waters could be 20 metres and so you could start to find this shallow water effect in waters which are perfectly viable for normal navigation. However as far as the change in the wave shape is concerned any effect will be barely noticeable until the depth of water is about half the wave length. This means that you could find a change in the character of the waves, a steepening of the gradient and a shortening of the wave length in depths of 10 metres which is still safe for general navigation. There is a certain element of safety in this situation because as the waves start to 'feel' the bottom this will give you early warning about the change in the wave conditions. Certainly the gradient of the wave is unlikely to approach the critical 18 degree angle until the wave is in comparatively shallow water, perhaps around 5 to 7 metres, but at this stage a lot will depend on the height of the wave which in turn depends on the strength of the wind. The stronger the wind, and hence the greater the height of the wave, the deeper the water in which the wave will start to rear up and become unstable. In practical terms this means that in more severe conditions it pays to give areas of shallow water a wider berth than normal because dangerous sea conditions and breaking waves could extend further seaward.

Waves Feel the Sea Bed

In inshore waters it doesn't require too much imagination to visualise the situations where breaking waves can occur because the water is shoaling, but a more sinister effect can be found in some sea areas a considerable distance away from land. In the case of a swell which has a 500 metre wave length the swell might be quite low in terms of wave height, perhaps just a metre or two, so its gradient will be very shallow in the open sea. Now if we consider that the water motion in such a wave could extend downwards for half of its wave length, it will start to 'feel' the bottom in depths of around 250 metres. Depths of 200 metres can be found a long way out from land, often near the edge of the Continental Shelf.

If we look around the Western Approaches of Britain the 200 metre depth contour can be found over 200 miles from land, and this is the point where these waves could start to show an increase in height and will start to slow down as the wave 'feels' the bottom. In normal circumstances these long swell waves would not have a great deal of influence on the overall sea conditions where the wind generated waves would predominate with their greater heights and shorter wave lengths. However, as these long swell waves start to hit the depths which for them are comparatively shallow water, the height of the wave increases and quite suddenly these seemingly innocuous waves can double or treble in height. Add this height factor on to the prevailing wind generated waves and you could find a significant area of more dangerous sea conditions.

This is a comparatively well known phenomenon found in areas around the Bay of Biscay and in the Western Approaches, where these long ocean swell waves meet the edge of the Continental Shelf. If these waves coincide with wind generated waves from already severe weather conditions, quite dangerous yet localised wave conditions can be generated which would not necessarily appear on any forecast chart of sea conditions.

What is 'Shallow'?

It was waves coming from such a source which are thought to have made conditions worse in some areas during the Fastnet storm of 1979. A study of the route of the yachts on this race shows that they would have passed over or close to the Lapadie Bank which is roughly midway between the Bishop Rock and Fastnet Lighthouses. Depths over this bank are around 90 metres compared with surrounding depths of 150 metres. South of the Lapadie Bank is an even shallower patch coming down to 50 metres, and there are several of these shallower patches to be found in the Western Approaches which could cause the longer wave length ocean waves to sense the bottom and generate more severe sea conditions than those which might already be prevailing in storm force conditions and thus lead to the extensive formation of translation waves.

Whilst translation waves are found generally in shallow water, the above examples show that the words 'shallow water' have to be used in a relative rather than absolute sense. Translation waves can be found wherever the sea becomes significantly shallower as you move downwind. This could be a beach or sandbank, the edge of the Continental Shelf or any shoal where the depth is equivalent to half the prevailing wave length or less, any sudden shoaling in fact where the waves can 'feel' the bottom; and therefore it should be possible to anticipate translation waves from a study of the chart. The wave length is the significant factor in deciding whether oscillation waves will turn into translation waves and start to break, and the longer the wave length the more likely the wave is to break in deeper water. Where there is a gradual change from deep water to shallow water, then the wave length of the wave will be gradually changed to reflect this and the change will normally be absorbed without the wave threatening to break. The more serious situation when waves are likely to break is when there is a sudden change in water depth, and the chart will throw out numerous examples of such areas which could well be areas to avoid when there are already rough sea conditions. Forecast charts showing swell predictions could be useful in trying to anticipate where these dangerous conditions could occur.

Pressure Waves

Pressure waves are those which are generated mainly by the passage of a large ship through the water. The waves are generated by what is called the wave-making resistance of the ship, and these create the familiar waves at bow and stern which run outward from the ship. Because they are generated by a one-time input of energy from the ship, such waves tend to decay fairly rapidly and they are unlikely to be felt more than about a mile from the ship which created them. In calm or near calm conditions it is quite easy to see these waves approaching and they are unlikely to present any particular hazard unless you are very close to the ship itself, but their danger lies primarily in the fact that they can arrive unannounced, and by being superimposed on the top of an existing wave pattern in lively sea conditions they could generate breaking waves in a local area.

Sailboats should be able to weather this type of breaking wave perhaps with a bit of discomfort and surprise, but otherwise with few lasting problems. These pressure waves are more likely to cause problems for planing powerboats which will have found a comfortable throttle setting for the prevailing sea conditions and which could be taken by surprise when they are suddenly hit by a pressure wave. This problem could be particularly pertinent at night time, when it is not always easy to assess the size of approaching waves. However, warning of the possibility of these pressure waves comes in the form of seeing other shipping in the vicinity. These pressure waves could cause local dangerous conditions if they arrive on top of an already rough sea when the mixing of the two wave trains could lead to high crests and breaking waves.

Clapotic Waves

The final type of wave is the clapotic wave. When two wave trains are travelling in different directions, the crests of the different wave trains will coincide at intervals along the wave crests. The combination of the two wave crests at these particular points will produce a higher than normal wave, and this combination will take the form of a pyramid shaped peak which is sometimes called a short crested wave.

Most yachtsmen at some time in their career will have come across these pyramid shaped waves which tend to rear up alongside the boat sometimes out of the blue and produce a frightening looking wave peak which can look as though it threatens to drop down on the yacht but which can disappear just as suddenly as it appeared.

In most cases where there are crossing wave trains of this type, the wave train being generated by the prevailing wind is far superior to the secondary wave train. This reduces the chance of a combination of wave crests producing a very high wave peak. You are less likely to find violent waves of this type in the open sea because there is usually a superior wave train which sets the main pattern, but there can be situations where intersecting wave trains are of the same or similar height and these can produce particularly dangerous and vicious sea conditions. The situation mentioned above where a long low swell meets shallow water and grows in stature is one. Another is where a wave train is approaching a vertical harbour wall or a cliff face which has relatively deep water alongside it. The approaching waves are not slowed because there is deep water and they hit the vertical wall and are reflected back from the wall at an angle which is equal to that at which they strike it. This generates a 'mirror image' set of waves. If the approaching wave train is parallel to the wall or cliff, then the reflected waves will also be parallel, whilst if the initial wave was at an angle of 45 degrees to the wall, then the reflected waves will also be at this same angle, producing two sets of waves which will then be crossing at 90 degrees to each other. The interaction between these two wave trains will produce what are called clapotic seas, the name reflecting the way in which the pyramid shaped waves are thrown up and often collapse in a welter of white water producing seas which can be particularly dangerous for small craft.

When clapotic waves are caused by cliffs it can be easy to escape from them by keeping further out to sea. When clapotic seas are generated by reflections off an exposed harbour wall you may meet them just when you are making your approach to harbour and when you might be starting to relax. Exposed artificial breakwaters are generally the main cause of clapotic seas in harbour approaches. These seas can be equally dangerous whether the wave trains are crossing at an angle or are parallel to each other. They have a viciousness about them which is rarely found in other types of wave, and you will often find that the yacht will have very little time to recover when trying to negotiate one of these towering crests before it is hit by the next. These areas of clapotic seas are certainly places to be avoided in fresh or strong winds, particularly when you may be tired at the end of a long passage and have less resilience to cope with them. Potential areas where these might be found can usually be identified from examination of the chart, but any exposed breakwaters should be suspect when the wind is blowing on to them.

Clapotic seas are less likely to be found in areas of steep cliffs because there is usually rubble at the foot of the cliffs which will help to absorb wave energy rather than reflect it. However there are some areas where cliffs run straight down into the sea without any cushioning rubble – one particular area is off the island of Hoy in the Orkney Islands where the cliffs are exposed to the full force of Atlantic gales, and they drop sheer into the water. Off a breakwater clapotic seas of any significance will rarely extend more than a mile from the breakwater itself, but from exposed cliffs the effects could be felt a couple of miles or more offshore.

Wave Refraction

Before we look at forecasting all these different types of waves, let us look at two more phenomena which can affect the behaviour of waves at sea. The first of these is refraction, a term usually associated with light passing through a lens or prism; but here we are talking about the way the direction of waves can be altered by their contact with land or shallow water. If you stand on the shore and watch waves approaching a beach from an angle it will help to understand refraction. Imagine that the wave front is approaching the shore from an angle of 45 degrees to the line of the beach. Despite this angle you will see that in the area where the waves actually break on the beach the waves are more or less parallel to the beach. The reason for this is refraction which causes the part of the approaching wave nearest the shore to be slowed down by the shallower water which allows the remaining part of the wave to 'catch up'. As the inshore end of the wave is slowed down, the rest of the wave is travelling faster and gradually the wave angles round to become virtually parallel with the beach more or less at the same time as it will break on to the beach. You are not particularly worried about what happens to a wave approaching a beach because you will not be in that vicinity in your yacht, but this refraction can be seen in other areas where it can have a significant effect on wave patterns.

Wave refraction around a headland can make what appears to be a sheltered anchorage vulnerable to swell coming into the bay. The refraction is caused by the wave slowing down in the shallow water inshore.

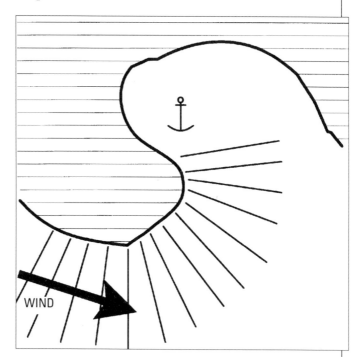

One of these effects can be found in areas where you might expect to find shelter: for example, behind that headland may not be quite the sheltered anchorage that you thought. The waves approaching the headland are slowed down at their inshore end and so the whole wave front gradually tends to swing round in a quite disconcerting way, through as much as 90 degrees or more, making you feel the waves have a mind of their own and are chasing you into what should have been a nice protected bay behind the headland. You can probably escape the effects of these refracted waves if you tuck yourself well in under the headland, where the waves will have dissipated a great deal of their energy by the time they reach your anchorage.

Possibly a more significant effect of refraction will be found behind islands and exposed shoals. Passing behind an island you might expect to find reasonably sheltered water and in many cases you could expect to find the same shelter from the waves behind an isolated shoal. It can be disconcerting to find that the conditions here can be even more lively and perhaps more dangerous than those on the weather side of the island or shoal. Once more it is refraction which is to blame and this will occur around both sides of the island or shallow water, bending the line of wave fronts through perhaps 30 or 40 degrees, so that by the time the two wave trains meet at the back of the island they are in fact crossing wave trains and you can find the dreaded clapotic seas as a result. The danger here is heightened because at first glance you might reasonably expect a degree of protection from the onslaught of the wind and the sea: you could be on passage and have suffered a problem with the mast or rigging and think that here is a place where you could stop and sort things out in relative calm, only to find that you have put added stress into the situation. You will probably find the shelter you want if you can tuck up close under the land.

Once you understand the refraction phenomenon then it is not too difficult to anticipate the problem as far as islands are concerned. With shoals it can be quite different because as we have seen, waves can be slowed down when the depth of water is reduced to half their wave length. This means that you could get refraction occurring around an isolated shoal where the depth of water was 20 metres and which seemed to pose no particular hazard to navigation. Yet that same 20 metre depth could cause refraction in an approaching wave train and so generate an area of crossing waves or clapotic seas extending some distance to leeward of the shoal. Such a situation is hard to predict because there are so many variables involved, the wave length and depth of water being perhaps the most significant, but the shape, extent and location of the shoal will also have a bearing on the outcome. Refraction of the waves around the Lapadie Bank may have been one of the factors affecting sea conditions during the 1979 Fastnet gale.

You can be sure that refracted waves will always be on the lee side of the shoal if they exist at all. The situation here is rather akin to the wind turbulence behind an island which can generate unexpected but quite

The refraction of the waves in this harbour entrance is demonstrated by the way they slow down on each shore and continue to advance in the centre to form a curved wave front.

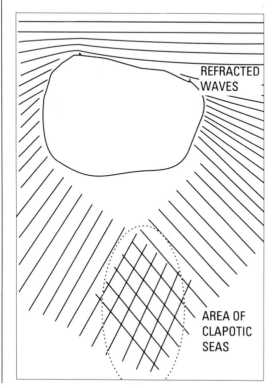

The way in which waves are refracted around an island or a shoal means that there can be crossing wave trains in the lee of the island creating potentially dangerous clapotic seas where you might logically expect to find shelter.

WIND AND SEA STATE

vicious squalls, and what it really means is that although the leeward side of land, island and shoals is generally looked on as the more benign area, both in terms of wind and sea conditions, you certainly mustn't take this for granted. You must be aware that both the wind and the waves have an insidious way of making themselves felt in areas where you might hope to escape them.

Tidal Streams and Currents

The other significant influence on both wave length and wave height, and consequently on the gradient, is tidal streams and currents. Where the whole body of water is moving, such as happens with a tidal stream or current, then the wave length will be shortened or lengthened depending on whether the tide or current is against the wind or with the wind. In general, currents can be separated out from tidal conditions because the currents flow in only one direction. In most cases a current is wind generated anyway, so the chances are that it will be flowing with the prevailing wind. When the wind and current are flowing in the same direction then this has the effect of increasing the wave length, with a consequent reduction in the gradient of the waves, and the sea conditions are thus more moderate than would otherwise be the case. This is certainly so as far as the effect of the wind on the current is concerned, but you also have to bear in mind that the current itself generates a degree of turbulence, particularly towards its edges where it comes into contact with water which is either slower-moving or stationary, and this turbulence itself can generate shorter, steeper wave patterns.

Should the wind flow be against the current or even across the current, then watch out for more difficult sea conditions because the wave length will tend to be shortened, and this produces steeper, more aggressive waves which can make life uncomfortable for small yachts. Currents rarely flow at more than one knot, and so the general effect of the current on sea conditions will be minimal, although it can certainly be noticeable in areas such as the Gulf Stream when crossing from Florida to the Bahamas. However, this is a particularly strong current area with the current running at two knots or more, which can be considered exceptional.

Wind Against Tide

While these effects have to be watched where localised currents do run strongly and where sea conditions can change quite noticeably with the wind direction, it is tides that tend to have a much more pronounced effect on the sea conditions. This is partly because the tidal flow tends to change direction every six hours or so, and partly because the difference in speed between one direction and the other could be up to eight knots and in extreme locations even up to twelve knots or more. Such a difference in the rate of tidal flow can have a profound effect on the waves generated, producing some of the most dangerous sea conditions to be found anywhere in the world.

Normally when the wind is generating waves a state of near equilibrium

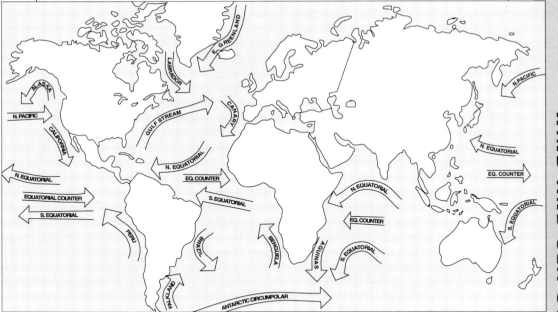

The principal ocean currents of the world, mainly generated by the prevailing winds.

is reached when the waves are of a height which can be supported by the prevailing wind. Now if the body of water is moving to windward, as would be the case when the wind is against the tide, two effects are noticed. Firstly, there is an apparent increase in the wind strength resulting from the wind and tide speeds working in opposition, and secondly, the progress of the waves to leeward is slowed. These two factors combined cause the wave length to be shortened considerably and shortening the wave length whilst maintaining the same wave height increases the gradient. Consequently there is a far higher risk of the waves breaking in these wind against tide conditions.

Wind against tide conditions are thus characterised by a very short, steep sea. Even in relatively light winds the sea can become quite uncomfortable, and because the crests are arriving in quick succession, it is very easy for a comparatively small boat to get out of step with the waves and not be able to recover fully from negotiating one wave before the next one is upon it. In stronger winds the short, steep seas will break, which can start to make the conditions very difficult and dangerous for a small yacht. The steep gradient will cause excessive pitching or rolling and there is the risk that should the vessel find the bow dropping as it tries to recover from negotiating one wave with a breaking crest, it may not necessarily be at the right angle to cope comfortably with the following wave, and a dangerous situation could be developing in which the boat could quite easily be overwhelmed with heavy seas breaking on board.

Another danger is that sea conditions in a wind against tide situation can deteriorate very rapidly as the tidal strength increases. In some areas where tides run strongly, the switch from the tide running with the wind to the tide running against the wind can take place within an hour and the change in sea conditions can be quite dramatic. From a comparatively calm, benign sea, very short, steep waves can be generated, resulting initially in a mass of 'white horses' – but as the tide gains strength and especially if the wind also increases, these 'white horses' can rapidly change to heavy breaking seas, or the type of overfalls which are often marked on the chart denoting dangerous sea areas.

When winds are approaching gale force any wind against tide condition is likely to produce quite severe sea conditions even when the tide is comparatively moderate. With tides of two knots or more in a gale of wind, you don't really want to risk these conditions because, unlike the open sea where shortening sail can usually resolve the situation where the wind is freshening, there is not a lot you can do to improve your lot in wind against tide seas except by running for shelter. The worst of such conditions can usually be avoided by studying the chart, either anticipating where they might occur or noting those marked as overfalls with the characteristic sign indicating breaking seas and dangerous sea conditions.

Tides in Narrow Waters

The areas around most headlands, where tides are inevitably stronger than they are inshore, are areas to be avoided when there is a strong wind and the tide is against the wind. If you have to pass through these areas then the logical thing to do is try and do so when the wind and tide are running together. Around some headlands it is possible to find a band of water very close inshore around the headland which is relatively free of these turbulent sea conditions. These inshore channels exist partly because the tide close inshore is often quite weak but also because the wind inshore may well be slowed by friction with the land. Certainly these friendly channels exist on many headlands but of course they are only viable for navigation if there are no dangerous shoal waters or rocks extending offshore, and also if you can get a safe approach to the inshore channel without having to go through turbulent waters to reach it. The existence of deep enough water can be identified from the chart but this is no guarantee that calmer conditions will prevail. The possibilities of such inshore channels when the wind is against the tide can only be found by experience or local knowledge.

Another situation where wind against tide conditions create particular problems can be found in many channels between offlying islands and the mainland, or similarly narrow areas where the tide might be accelerated through channels between sandbanks. You can expect to find turbulent sea conditions anywhere that strong tides exist, and indeed in some of these areas which have an evil reputation amongst seamen, the pilot book will often describe the conditions as 'akin to maelstrom conditions'. The message here is loud and clear and it is that you should not attempt these conditions in a yacht unless the wind and tide are in harmony or the wind is very light. In some narrow channels the turbulent conditions can extend right across the channel leaving nowhere clear for a small boat to find a way, whilst in others a clear passage may be found around one end or the other where the tides may be weak. You have to remember when considering these passages between islands and the mainland that not only does the tide become accelerated and run strongly through these channels but the wind can also be accelerated considerably, as we discussed in the last chapter, and this combination means difficult conditions when the wind and tide are in opposition.

Tide Races

So far we have looked at effects of wind and tide, shallow water and clapotic seas in isolation, but of course in many cases they will appear in combination and this is when the most difficult and dangerous conditions will be found. It doesn't require too much imagination to picture the situation where there is a gale of wind running against a strong tide with shallow water or islands interfering with the free tidal flow. Such locations and conditions could be totally untenable for small craft. The Pentland Firth is one such area. Here the North Sea meets the Atlantic Ocean in a tempestuous relationship with tides flowing at up to ten knots which in itself is enough to generate ferocious sea conditions, particularly when the wind is against the tide. Added to these extremely strong tides are the islands located across the Firth which interfere with the tidal flow. When seen from the air the islands seem to have a bow wave around them because in effect they are 'steaming' through the tidal flow. From the air it is possible to see the turbulent flow of water which exists in the lee of the islands, just like the wake of a ship, and this is an area where even on a calm day the effects of the turbulence generated by strong tides can make life very uncomfortable for small craft.

The notorious 'race' areas which are marked on charts or commented on in pilot books are usually the result of a combination of circumstances which lead to a rapid deterioration of conditions. Some of these can occur when two tidal streams meet, as is the case with the Alderney Race where the tides flowing up between the island of Alderney and the Cherbourg peninsula meet the main tidal stream flowing up or down the English Channel. This on its own would be enough to generate increased turbulence in the water but added to this are the refracted waves flowing round the island of Alderney and the fact that the tidal stream between this island and the mainland is compressed into a narrow area, resulting in lively and potentially dangerous sea conditions at various states of the tide.

The Portland Race is another example and here the race is primarily caused by the way this headland juts out into the tidal stream. The suddenness with which the tidal flow has to divert to sweep around the headland means that considerable turbulence is created in the tidal flow and this initiates the race conditions. The flow is further complicated by the eddies which are created in the lee of the headland and these circular eddies mean that tidal flow is running back into the main stream creating further turbulence. What is interesting about this particular race is that it extends a long way offshore, up to seven or eight miles, demonstrating just how severe the impact on the tidal stream is by such a dramatic headland. However, there is a clear channel inside the tide race, which allows passage to be made in reasonable sea conditions even when the main tide race just offshore is producing maelstrom conditions. This inside passage is no more than 300 metres wide and you need to follow the headland close inshore to avoid the eddy effect in the lee of Portland Bill.

A similar but less severe tide race occurs off the Lizard, which is a very pronounced headland, but here there is no inside passage available because there are rocks running up to half a mile offshore and the race starts immediately the rocks stop. This demonstrates how you need to study closely the geography of the headland and the surrounding waters in order to make an assessment of the likely conditions. Although the Lizard peninsula is probably just as dramatic as Portland Bill in the way it juts out into the tidal flow, the Lizard race itself is less severe, probably because the patches of rock running out from the headland help to absorb and slow the impact on the tidal flow.

The combination of shallow water and tidal streams can be seen in many areas around the North Sea and in some parts of the English Channel. The St Alban's Race off the Dorset coast is a good example of the way shallow water can force the upwelling of the tidal flow to create turbulence. This is visible as a narrow band of breaking waves which may be only two or three waves wide but extends a considerable way out to seaward in line with the shoal. The actual location of the breaking waves will vary with the tide, being mainly on the down-tide section of the shoal but of course considerably exaggerated when there are wind against tide conditions. In the North Sea there are extensive sandbanks but these are almost invariably below the water. Their location is marked by the turbulent conditions generated by the tide but fortunately here the turbulence rarely extends out far from the edge of the sandbank or shoal water, so that it leaves the main channels clear.

Forecasting Sea Conditions in Coastal Waters
Trying to assess conditions in these coastal waters requires a careful interpretation of the weather forecast and the tide tables. Tidal atlases can also be a great help because they show the flow of the tidal streams at different states of the tide, but the actual wave conditions can be estimated only from personal experience. The wave heights in some of these difficult coastal areas are not likely to be much greater than those of surrounding areas of sea but it is the gradient which generally changes quite dramatically, so that not only are the wave crests much closer together but they are much more likely to break. The characteristic of these turbulent sea areas is the white breaking water and the sheer unpredictability of the waves. The unpredictability comes from the fact that often in these areas

there are crossing wave trains which generate high peaks and transient waves, and if you get into these waters with a small craft, you can come out feeling almost punch drunk. It is really not so much a question of forecasting what it might be like in these turbulent waters, but much more of forecasting where these turbulent conditions can occur so that you can keep well clear of them. Entering these turbulent areas is to court disaster and even well found boats may not be equal to these conditions.

Standard Definitions of Sea State			
Height of waves *(metres)*			Sea State
0			calm, glassy
0	to	0.1	calm, rippled
0.1	to	0.5	smooth
0.5	to	1.25	slight
1.25	to	2.5	moderate
2.5	to	4	rough
4	to	6	very rough
6	to	9	high
9	to	14	very high
		over 14	phenomenal

Wave heights and the terms which are used to describe them in weather reports and forecasts.

The sort of conditions you will frequently need to forecast are those to be expected when the tide turns and the wind and tide are in opposition. This can happen over all sea areas where there are tidal streams, and there can also be significant changes in areas with strong currents when the wind blows against the current. In this situation it will be the wind direction which is the critical factor and if you see this type of weather pattern developing, then the best way to try and anticipate the change in sea conditions is to imagine the wind strength increasing by one or two numbers on the Beaufort Scale – this will give you some idea of the increased severity of the sea conditions that you can expect to find. With tidal flows the changing conditions can be much more severe, partly because the tides often run much more strongly than the average current does, but also because when wind and tide are together the wave length is stretched out and in effect the sea is moderated in these conditions. So in trying to assess how the change of tide will affect the sea conditions you will probably need to add two or three numbers on the Beaufort Scale to try and get a mental picture of the severity of the seas.

It is easy to see from this why weather forecasts shy away from predicting wave heights for coastal waters where strong tidal streams exist. It would be rare to find a forecast that gives much indication of sea conditions in northern European waters. In the Mediterranean and around most of the USA wave heights are more predictable and are often

WIND AND SEA STATE

included in coastal weather forecasts, but even here forecasters tend to hedge their bets quite strongly, so in the USA you could well find the forecaster suggesting wave heights of 4 to 6 feet, or in the Mediterranean it could be 1 to 1.5 metres. These top and bottom figures span a considerable range of sea conditions, from reasonably comfortable to decidedly uncomfortable conditions, indicating not just that the forecaster is not being very positive but perhaps more importantly that sea conditions can vary considerably from place to place depending on the shelter from the land or the fetch and the prevailing wind direction. No forecast of sea conditions will give an indication of the wave gradient because this can vary so much with local conditions. Yet it is the gradient which is the single most significant factor concerning waves as far as yachts are concerned, and you have to judge this for yourself.

Forecasting Sea Conditions in Deep Waters
Forecasting sea conditions in the open ocean has become a much more positive affair, but even here there is still a considerable element of vagueness, certainly in comparison with forecasts of wind strength. You might think that in the open ocean, wind strength and wave height were more or less directly related and this is certainly the case in theory. The tables show the direct relationship between fetch, wind strength and time but the big problem is that there is a considerable degree of randomness about waves, and about wave height and gradients in particular. In any train of waves generated by a consistent wind, a wide variety of wave heights will be experienced even over a comparatively short time. In generating his forecast of wave heights, the forecaster is only taking into account the waves generated by the prevailing wind. However waves do not die away suddenly and can persist for a considerable period of time after the wind has stopped sustaining them. These dying wave trains are called the swell and initially they may not be much different from the wind generated waves, but gradually their height diminishes and if there is no further wind blowing to generate a new wave pattern then these waves translate into the familiar long ocean swell.

The difficulties in forecasting wave height come when the remains of one wave train have a second and developing wave train imposed on top of them from a new wind from a different direction. Now you have two wave trains crossing which will generate a form of clapotic sea. This will not be as severe as that created by reflected waves but these crossing wave trains, one dying away and one growing in stature under the influence of the prevailing wind, will introduce an element of randomness into the wave heights and gradients. This can create a variety of different waves, some combining and peaking into waves of considerable stature, others cancelling each other out and creating relatively smooth patches. It is almost impossible to anticipate just what the wave conditions are going to be with these crossing wave trains except that there will be a degree of randomness about the height, size and gradient of the waves. Bear in mind also that you are probably fortunate if there are only two wave trains

| Wind speed | Fetch (nautical miles) ----> | | | | | |
(knots)	10	50	100	300	500	1,000
10	2	2	2	2	2	2
15	3	4	5	5	5	5
20	4	7	8	9	9	9
30	6	13	16	18	19	20
40	8	18	23	30	33	34
50	10	22	30	44	47	51

Above: How the fetch, or distance to windward of the nearest land, will affect the wave height in different wind speeds.

Right: A graph showing the approximate relationship between wave height, fetch and wind speed. Given the wind speed and the fetch, it is possible to get a good idea of what the average wave height might be.

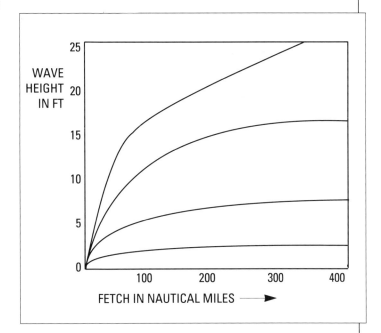

FETCH IN NAUTICAL MILES ---->

| Wind speed | Duration (hours) | | | | | | |
(knots)	5	10	15	20	30	40	50
10	2	2	2	2	2	2	2
15	4	4	5	5	5	5	5
20	5	7	8	8	9	9	9
30	9	13	16	17	18	19	19
40	14	21	25	28	31	33	33
50	19	29	36	40	45	48	50
60	24	37	47	54	62	67	69

The wave heights in feet which can be expected from different wind speed over varying lengths of time.

WIND AND SEA STATE

WIND AND SEA STATE

crossing. There could be three or four, in which case trying to forecast wave height and conditions can become very difficult.

Significant Wave Height

From this you might think it was almost impossible to forecast wave height. However, there is almost invariably one predominant wave train which sets the pattern, and this is usually what the forecasters are talking about in their forecast of wave height – but even then, if you look at the recordings of wave conditions from wave recorders mounted on buoys or ships you will see a considerable variation of wave heights within a particular wave train. The forecasters try to make the expected sea conditions more comprehensible by using what they call the significant wave height as the basis of their forecast.

Significant wave height, as we mentioned briefly in Chapter 3, is defined as the average of the highest one-third of the waves passing a particular point. This height has been selected because it tends to agree reasonably well with the wave heights reported by experienced observers on board ships when they are trying to estimate the average height of the highest of the waves in a particular wave pattern. Forecasters use the significant wave height because it will conjure up a particular picture in the minds of experienced mariners and they will know what the forecaster has in mind.

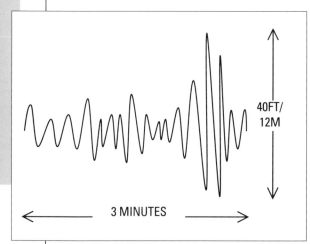

Typical trace from a wave recorder which shows how much larger waves can be found in a generally moderate wave train.

What the significant wave height does not tell you is the maximum height of waves which might be found in a wave pattern; yet it is this height which often exercises the minds of yachtsmen and there is considerable concern about the occurrence of 'freak' waves which are part of the folklore of going to sea. The term 'freak' tends to suggest that these more extreme waves are totally unexpected and unpredictable, but this is not quite true. One has only to look at the statistics from wave recorders to recognise that these higher than normal waves do exist and that they are definable.

Very Large Waves

There are various figures which relate to these so called 'freak' waves, and one commonly quoted value forecasts the highest wave which may pass a particular point over a ten minute period. Research suggests that this highest wave will be 1.6 times the significant wave height. If you take a three hour period then the highest wave experienced in that time could be twice the significant wave height. These statistics themselves can be quite frightening and, put another way, they suggest that one wave in every 23 will be twice the average height, one wave in 1,175 will be three times the average height, and one wave in every 300,000 will be four times the average height. Note here that the statistics are talking about the *average* wave height and not the significant wave height. Nonetheless, they give food for thought.

These statistics are certainly worth bearing in mind when you are at sea in rough weather because they emphasise the need always to keep something in hand rather than push your boat to the limits. However they do need to be put into perspective. Firstly, the average height of a wave train is lower than you might think. We tend to judge the sea solely by the larger waves we encounter, as it is these waves which have a greater impact, and we tend to forget or ignore the smaller waves. Waves of twice the average height would probably be included among the larger waves which registered in our minds when trying to estimate the height of waves at sea. This is why the significant wave height has been established as a yardstick because it gives a better indication of the larger waves normally encountered in an average sea.

Secondly, if you take a wave period of 10 seconds, which can be fairly average in rough seas, then this means that there are 6 waves a minute, 360 waves an hour, and 8,640 waves per 24 hours passing a given point. This means that the chance of meeting that one wave in 300,000 which is four times the average height, is fairly remote, particularly bearing in mind that these waves tend to be transient rather than travel as huge waves over long distances. However statistics are one thing and reality is another, and that wave four times higher than average could be just waiting around the corner as the next wave, rather than one perhaps 300,000 waves away. We talk about experiencing freak waves which come out of the blue, but 'rogue waves' might be a better term to use and the biggest problem faced by those experiencing these waves is perhaps not so much the actual height of the wave, but whether it is breaking or not. A very large wave appearing out of the blue on its own is not particularly dangerous if the gradient of the wave is still similar to that of the smaller waves. Where the risks occur is when this larger than normal wave is generated with a wave length similar to that of the smaller waves. Then of course the gradient steepens dramatically and suddenly this larger than normal wave is also a breaking wave, and this is when trouble can start. As these large waves tend to be generated from a combin-ation of existing wave peaks which are superimposed one on top of the other to create the extra height, then they can occur with a short wave length and a very steep gradient and that is when you can get into severe difficulties.

Out in the sea where the waves are not generally breaking except for the comparatively gentle action of 'white horses' and similar instability, the

This graph gives some indication of the maximum height of waves you might expect to find after the wind had been blowing for some time. Constant strong winds can generate higher waves, so after 30 hours of constant wind you could find waves 1.4 times the expected height.

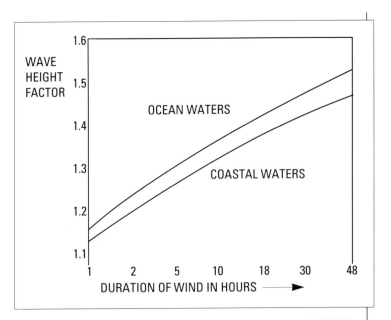

appearance of a larger than normal wave with a near vertical face and a breaking crest is the sort of stuff that nightmares are made of and it is easy to see why such a wave gets the term 'freak'. However such waves are almost invariably transient and may not sustain themselves for longer than a few seconds. Often they will rear up alongside in frightening fashion but disappear almost as quickly as they came, and you have to be unlucky indeed to be in that particular spot where

Wind speed *(knots)*	Wave height *(feet)*
8	3
12	5
16	8
19	12
27	20
31	25
35	30
39	36
43	39
47	45
51	51

The probable maximum height of waves found at sea with various wind strengths when there is an unlimited fetch.

this transient wave curls over and breaks – but no doubt it is the occurrence of being in the wrong place at the wrong time which accounts for some of the yachts which disappear at sea without trace. It is also worth bearing in mind that just as these large waves can be found at sea, so can deep troughs or holes between the waves. With large waves you get a degree of warning except perhaps at night, but with the deep troughs you don't see them until you start to drop into them. The climb out of a deep trough can seem like an eternity, particularly if the far crest appears about to break.

Forecasting Wave Heights

Weather forecasts now routinely give wave heights for ocean areas and these can arrive either in the form of figures in a radio weather forecast or lines of equal wave height on a weatherfax forecast. The height of sea waves is determined by assessing firstly the wind speed and the duration of this wind, and finally the fetch, which is the distance at sea over which the wind has been blowing uninterrupted. The wind speed is determined from the distance apart of the isobars and is part of the normal forecasting routine, whilst the duration has to be established because it takes time for a wave pattern to build up to maturity. If a constant wind has been blowing for a long period, then the wind speed can be used directly to determine the value of the significant wave height which will be produced. If the wind has varied over this long period, say 48 hours which would normally be the case, then an average value of the wave height has to be assumed. Any forecast of wave height has to make a lot of compromises and averages, and the modern computer assessments of wave height are remarkably accurate in terms of the average conditions which they forecast. When making plans and assessing these forecasts it is important to bear in mind that they do relate to average conditions and average wave heights, and that amongst these averages you can find all sorts of extremes, in the same way that the forecast of winds tends to concentrate on the consistent winds that are blowing, rather than the gusts which might occur.

There is a considerable similarity between the forecasting of winds and the forecasting of wave conditions, and indeed any wind forecast tends to be directly related to the waves that such winds could be assumed to generate. With computer forecasting it is also possible to make an assessment of the decay of these waves as the wind reduces or changes direction, and modern forecasts can also include forecasts of the swell conditions which might be experienced. Forecasts of wave conditions are significant when it comes to weather routeing because it is the wave heights which tend to limit the progress of shipping. Wave heights affect the progress of yachts as well, and extreme conditions are obviously to be avoided as far as possible, so these forecasts of wave height which can extend to three or in some cases five days in advance can be a significant tool in planning any long distance voyages. It should be borne in mind that these forecasts of wave height are only averages so they must be treated with a degree of caution. In coastal waters there are many extreme conditions which can be generated by wind and tide working in combination or in opposition, whilst both here and in the open sea there is always the risk that much larger waves than average will be encountered. In other words always try and keep something in reserve, because the forecast tends to represent the average rather than the extremes, and it is the extremes which can cause you problems and possibly damage.

7 Poor Visibility

Even in this age where electronics provide us with so much navigation information, the ability to check the information that the electronics are producing is still vital to give the navigator peace of mind. It is possible to make a landfall using radar and electronic position fixing, but if visibility is poor there is always a considerable sigh of relief when the land is actually sighted. Then you can feel much more comfortable that the electronics are doing their job properly. When it comes to entering or leaving harbour you are pushing the capabilities of electronics to their limits if you have to do this in poor visibility. In almost everything we do at sea good visibility is critical for keeping good safety margins, so the visibility forecast is vital information for the navigator.

Despite the importance of knowing what the visibility is going to be, estimating the visibility is one of the hardest parts of the weather forecaster's job. This can be particularly the case out at sea where there is only a limited number of weather reports coming in from light vessel or buoy reporting stations, or from ships themselves. Because many of these reporting stations are now automatic, there may be no actual reports of what the current visibility is in that locality, because it is difficult to measure without human assistance. Then again the conditions which reduce visibility can often be the result of quite critical conditions and it may need only a small change in these conditions to make the difference between good visibility and bad. To make the situation more complicated there can be a number of different reasons for the visibility being reduced, amongst them being various types of mist or fog, rain, drizzle, snow and so on, all of which tend to make life very difficult for the weather forecaster and the navigator.

Even when it is possible to predict that visibility will be reduced because of the conditions found in the forecast, many of these conditions may be quite local in nature or extent, and one of the hardest jobs of the forecaster is to cope with these local conditions whilst producing a general weather forecast. For instance, a forecaster may suggest that there will be showers of rain which will almost certainly reduce the visibility within those showers, but how can you determine whether you are going to have these showers in your immediate locality and whether they are going to pass between your yacht and the land or out to sea? Fog and mist can be equally problematic in trying to establish just where they will strike, because the conditions necessary for fog or mist to form rely mainly on quite small temperature variations which can change from one mile to the next. It might be easier to forecast poor visibility when the conditions are such that large areas are going to be affected, as could happen with extensive rain during the passage of a front or where the conditions are so positively in favour of fog developing, that the fog banks will be extensive. At the other extreme, there are the obviously clear conditions when the risks of poor visibility are minimal and the forecaster can be equally positive. It's the bits in between which make life difficult, when there are showers or intermittent rain, when the rain may be light enough not to impair seriously the visibility or when there are showers or intermittent rain or snow where the visibility range could go up and down varying with both time and position. This is where you have to take over from the forecaster and try and make an assessment of the local potential for visibility limits, just as you have to in trying to fine-tune the wind and sea forecasts.

In order to do this we need to see how the various types of fog are formed, to look at where rain can be expected to reduce the visibility and where drizzle may be found within particular weather patterns. As with most things which affect the weather, proximity to the land can often have a profound effect on conditions. In this respect fog is particularly insidious in that it is much more likely to form in areas just where the navigation is at its trickiest, so knowing whether it is probable can have a significant bearing on your plans.

Two Types of Fog

There are two main types of fog found at sea. One is radiation fog which is generally formed as a result of the cooling of the land at night time. Although it is essentially a land-based fog it often drifts out to sea in coastal and estuary waters. The second main type is advection fog, which is often called a sea fog and is formed by warm moist air blowing in over colder water. For both of these types of fog, particular sets of conditions are necessary for the fog to form. Before we look at these in more detail it is worth considering just what fog is.

There is no difference between fog and mist except one of degree. In meteorological terms fog is any reduction in visibility below one kilometre or half a sea mile. Mist is any reduction in visibility above this figure with a top visibility limit of one mile, but the actual causes of the reduction in visibility are exactly the same in both cases. Most air found at sea contains water vapour to a certain degree. This water vapour generally comes from evaporation of water from the surface of the ocean or from air passing over wet land, and the amount of this water vapour that the air can hold without the water vapour condensing will vary with temperature. In general the higher the temperature the more water vapour the air can hold. This water vapour contained in the air is completely clear and transparent, so whilst it remains in vapour form it has no effect on visibility. It is only when this water vapour reaches saturation point, which is the maximum amount of water vapour which can be contained in any particular volume of air, that there is a risk of this water vapour condensing. This will happen if there is any drop in temperature of the air or if the air comes into contact with air, water or land which is colder.

We see this going on all the time with clouds, which are simply air that has been saturated with water vapour and has come into contact with air of a lower temperature. This causes the water vapour to condense into tiny droplets which are not heavy enough to drop as rain, but which form into clouds. It is the degree of moisture in the air and the relative temperatures which are critical to the formation of cloud, and generally a degree of turbulence is also required in order to get two types of air, warm and cold, to mix and so reduce the temperature and generate the cloud. This is why we invariably see cloud at frontal areas where warm and cold air masses are mixing.

We will go into the different types of cloud later on, but in terms of fog much the same sort of thing happens, although instead of moist air mixing with colder air, fog or mist usually forms when the moist air comes into contact with a cold land or sea surface. The three conditions generally considered necessary for the formation of fog are firstly a supply of sufficiently moist air close to saturation point to bring in the water vapour, secondly a cold surface which can be either the land or the sea, and thirdly a degree of turbulence to ensure that the moist air moves in over the cold surface. This last factor seems to indicate the need for wind, but in fact the amount of wind necessary to generate the turbulence can be very, very light indeed and with radiation fog it is not required.

Radiation Fog

For the first type of fog then, radiation or ground fog, it is the cooling of the land surface at night time which provides the cold surface. The air in contact with the ground is cooled below its dew point, or the point at which the water vapour will condense, and this means that the excess water vapour within the air is condensed, forming fog. Although the fog forms over the land it can often drift out to sea, but it will usually disperse when it comes into contact with a comparatively warm water surface which will generally be no more than a mile or two offshore. Radiation fog can extend up to ten miles off the coast in extreme circumstances but this is the exception rather than the rule. Radiation fog tends to be associated with the type of conditions prevailing in anti-cyclones or areas of high pressure. It is these weather patterns which provide the clear skies and the light winds which are necessary for the initial formation of the fog.

In temperate climates radiation or ground fog is generally a feature of autumn and winter weather because during these periods the air tends to be moist and the nights are long, which allows for more extensive cooling. For radiation fog to clear it needs the warmth of the sun to raise the temperature of both the air and land so that the air temperature then rises above the dew point and the condensed water turns back into water

Above: Radiation fog in a belt along the coast. This fog was already in the clearance stage and had already burnt off from the sea.
Below: Radiation fog clearing and thinning in the morning to reveal the hidden headland.

vapour. In the winter when the sun's rays are generally weak and there is only limited heating power, radiation fog can be slow to clear and it can persist right through the day and get thicker again as night falls. Given a period of settled anti-cyclone conditions it is possible for radiation fog to persist for several days during the winter.

Radiation fog tends to start just before or just after dawn. This is when the night temperatures are at their lowest and it is often a period when the wind is at a minimum or even dies away completely. Because the sun's rays just after dawn start the slow process of warming the land, the heat generated starts to produce an element of turbulence into the air. At this time the temperature has not risen enough for the fog to disperse and the slight turbulence will often mean that the radiation fog can start to thicken up just after dawn. In general the maximum intensity of radiation fog is found about an hour after sunrise, whilst the minimum intensity, if the fog has persisted all day, is likely to be in the early afternoon.

Where Radiation Fog is Likely

As you can imagine, radiation fog can be localised and there are some particular areas where the fog is much more likely to occur than others. One of these is in the vicinity of industrial areas and many large cities. In these areas you can find a high level of smoke pollution and the tiny particles of the smoke pollution provide a high count of the small nuclei which help the water condensation process to start. In these conditions the condensing of the water vapour can start even before the relative humidity of the water vapour in the air has reached 100 per cent. Another feature of this radiation fog found in industrial areas is that it can have a yellow or brownish tinge which converts the normal white fog into what is known as 'smog'. Fog of this type can often persist for several days, particularly when the air conditions are relatively calm and stable.

Radiation fog is also more pronounced in sheltered areas because here the cooling of the land at night tends to be more pronounced than in places which are exposed to the wind. However, such sheltered areas are less likely to be found along the coast and a more sinister effect will be found in valleys and low lying ground where colder air formed over higher land tends to roll down into the valley as a katabatic wind. This cold air coming down at night time can be further cooled as it comes down the valley allowing the water vapour to condense and the air will then roll out to sea as a bank of fog.

Marsh areas can be particularly prone to radiation fog because here you have the combination of the high humidity created by the water content of the marshy areas combined with the vegetation of the marsh, which allows the heat to radiate away from these areas rapidly during the night. Such marshy areas are often found adjacent to rivers, harbours and estuaries and can lead to fog in these local areas whilst it is still quite clear out at sea.

A characteristic of radiation fog is that it is usually very shallow in depth because it is only the air in contact with or close to the ground which gets cooled sufficiently for the water vapour to condense. It may be possible to get a clear view from the top of a mast, though you will only see other craft which have similar tall masts.

So, summing up radiation fog, the conditions necessary for this fog to form are clear nights with little or no cloud, so that radiation from the land can take place to produce rapid cooling; the air needs to be relatively moist so that it requires only a small reduction in temperature for the water vapour to condense; and finally winds have to be fairly light, with a speed of about five knots producing the ideal conditions which help to diffuse the surface cooling of the land through a sufficient volume of air to start the fog. Looking at the other side for the conditions in which such a fog will disperse, there is firstly the heating of the land by the sun, which will in turn warm the air which is in contact with the land. This increases the capacity of this air to hold more water vapour, so that in turn the fog is evaporated and disperses. Another situation which will help radiation fog to disperse is the freshening of the wind which increases the turbulence so that the colder air in contact with the land is mixed with warmer air from above and the fog evaporates and is carried away as water vapour.

Advection Fog
Advection fog is formed when warm, moist air passes over a cold surface. This type of fog is generally known as sea fog when the cold surface is provided by the sea. One of the most significant differences between this sea fog and radiation fog is the fact that sea fog will often be found when there are moderate winds blowing, something which never happens with radiation fog. This is one way to tell the difference between the two and indeed a wind is one of the necessary criteria for a sea fog to develop because the warm, moist air has to blow in over the cold sea. Whilst the still conditions associated with radiation fog are what you expect for fog over land, there is something very eerie about a situation when the wind may be blowing Force 4 or 5 and there are moderate seas running and this is combined with greatly reduced visibility. It creates a very uncomfortable set of weather circumstances for yachts.

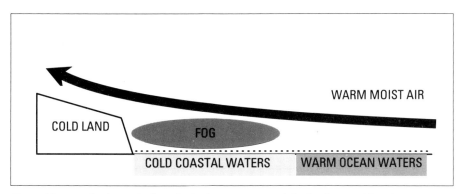

Coastal fog can be formed when the inshore waters and the land are cold and a warmer moist air sweeps in from the sea.

POOR VISIBILITY

The actual physical processes involved in the formation of sea fog are similar to those found with radiation fog. The warm, moist air has to come into contact with a surface whose temperature is below the dew point of this nearly saturated air, so that when the air becomes cool in contact with the colder surface, the water vapour condenses and the fog forms. The main difference between radiation fog and sea fog is in the nature of the cooling surface. The temperature of the surface of the sea will vary only slightly from day to night, through heating by the sun and through loss of heat by radiation at night time, and the temperature of the sea surface varies very little from day to day. This means that the occurrence of sea fog tends not to depend either on the time of the day or the state of the sky and it doesn't need the clear skies which are a characteristic of the formation of radiation fog. Sea fogs can often persist for considerable periods even though the warm, moist air might be expected to warm the surface of the sea. The same wind that brings the moist air in over the colder sea tends to stir up the surface of the sea, which in turn brings colder water to the surface so that even under the influence of the warm air the actual temperature of the sea surface changes very little. These sea fogs can persist until there is significant change in the conditions and this usually means a change in the direction of the wind which in turn will bring in wind with reduced humidity and moisture content.

Sea fog will often be comparatively shallow in extent, maybe extending for only ten metres above the surface of the sea. At times the base of the fog may not rest on the sea surface, and there could be a metre or so of clear air immediately above the waterline. It can be possible to take advantage of these characteristics by placing a lookout either very low or high up the mast when it may be possible to get extended visibility, but again the lookout above the fog will only be able to see the masts of other vessels which are sufficiently tall to show up through the fog.

Where Advection Fog is Likely
Sea fog is practically unknown in tropical waters and is much more a feature of temperate and high latitude areas where cold water currents exist. In these areas it generally occurs in the spring or early summer when the sea is still cold, and the air passing over it can be relatively warm and moist, either because it has originated in lower latitudes or it has passed over warmer land masses which start to get heated with the arrival of spring. There are certain areas of the world which are particularly prone to sea fogs.

British Isles
A sea fog can be found frequently in the English Channel and its approaches, particularly in the spring and early summer and it occurs when warm, damp air is brought in from the vicinity of the Azores by south westerly winds. In the English Channel the fog is likely to be more prevalent when the wind is west or south west, whilst in the Irish Sea it can be more prevalent when the wind is south or south west, these wind

directions relating to the general run of the sea areas involved. In the North Sea, sea fog is likely to be more prevalent with easterly winds which are blowing off the heated continental mainland.

East Coast of North America
This region probably has more sea fog than any other in the world with these fogs occurring over 50 per cent of the time during June and July. The reason for these fogs is the reduction of the sea temperature caused by the cold Labrador current which heads southward from Greenland and tracks over the Grand Banks and down the Eastern Seaboard. Here it can come into contact with the warm, moist south westerly winds which are responsible for the Gulf Stream. Alternatively in the spring and summer the heated land mass of the North American continent can provide the warmer winds which will be the catalyst for fog over the colder sea areas, particularly on the Grand Banks of Newfoundland, although these winds off the land tend to hold less moisture than the sea winds.

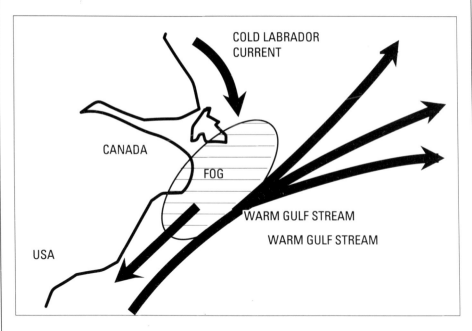

Fog can occur for 50 per cent of the time over the eastern seaboard of the USA in the summer months. The reason is that the cold Labrador current heading south inshore meets the warm moist air associated with the Gulf Stream.

North West Pacific
The north west Pacific conditions are very similar to those found off the east coast of North America. Here it is the cold Kamchatka current which provides the cold water, and again it is either wind coming off the warming land mass to the west of this cold sea area or the warm, moist air

coming from the south east where there are much higher sea surface temperatures which provides the second ingredient necessary for the formation of sea fog.

Cold Water Coasts
There are several areas in the world where cold water currents pass close to land masses which are warmer or which are affected by the trade winds. The Californian coast is one such area whilst the coast of Chile, the south west coast of Africa and Morocco are other areas where sea fogs can be found.

Other Types of Fog
Sea fog and radiation fog are the two main types of fog which will be experienced by yachts, but there are a number of other types of fog, some peculiar to particular parts of the world, others due to particular winds or local conditions.

Smoke Fog
On its own, smoke is not generally responsible for fog although forest fires or similar extensive fires could reduce visibility locally. Smoke fog tends to be called 'smog' which has already been mentioned as a form of radiation fog which is more likely to occur in industrial areas or around large urban conurbations. With a general reduction of atmospheric pollution this type of fog is a less familiar occurrence although in areas such as Los Angeles this 'smog' is becoming a characteristic feature owing to the pollution from motor vehicles.

Dust Fog
Dust fog embraces a variety of causes of reduction in visibility, such as sand storms. The poor visibility is caused by the atmosphere being full of dust and this can be found in sea areas adjacent to deserts or other dry areas, and is usually related to the squally wind conditions which are found with the passage of a cold front. The dust in these storms can be very light and can travel considerable distances, so that off the west coast of Africa dust can reduce visibility up to one hundred miles off the coastline if the wind conditions are favourable. The same can happen off the south east coast of Australia with the hot, dry wind known as the Britfielder.

Warm Water Fog
This type of fog is something like the reverse of sea fog. It occurs when cold air blows over a relatively warm sea. Warm water fog is generally associated with the polar regions but it can also be found on rivers and lakes in cold weather. This type of fog is often transitory and tends to have the appearance of smoke or steam rising from the water, hence its alternative name of 'seasmoke'. It is caused by cold air condensing moisture in the air layer close to the warm water.

Mixing Fog

This fog is formed by the contact of warm air and a cold sea surface, or sometimes the other way round, but it can also be caused by warm air meeting cold air. This type of mixing is a feature of frontal systems and whilst in most cases the mixing results in the characteristic cloud formations associated with frontal systems, particularly those of the warm front, this mixing can also produce fog. This mixing fog can occur in fresh wind conditions, though such conditions are more likely to develop cloud rather than fog close to the sea surface. This mixing fog tends to be more associated with weaker warm fronts, which in turn tends to mean that the fog could occur at the outer extremity of the warm front rather than in the more active sections nearer the centre of depression. Such mixing fogs can persist for some time if the frontal system itself is stationary, but otherwise as the front passes through the fog will disperse.

Drizzle

Drizzle is the sort of half way house between fog and rain. Drizzle comes under the category of rain because the water droplets are actually falling whereas in fog the much smaller water droplets are held suspended in the air. Whilst drizzle is like rain in that the water droplets are falling, these water droplets are very small compared with rain and they have the effect of cutting down on visibility quite seriously. Visibility ranges of less than half a mile can often be characteristic of drizzle conditions. This brings it into the danger zone as far as visibility is concerned, which is why drizzle has been brought in here. It tends to be associated with low overcast skies, although it can also be associated with broken cloud which tends to create intermittent drizzle. The drizzle associated with heavy overcast skies tends to occur towards the centre of a depression in its warm air sector, which in the northern hemisphere lies to the south of the centre. Drizzle conditions can be found throughout this warm air sector of a depression, but the further away from the centre, the more likely that the drizzle will be intermittent and occur more in the form of showers. In European waters drizzle is most associated with winds coming from the south west, or west south west, whereas on the eastern coast of North America it tends to be the south easterly winds which bring the drizzle. These are the same winds which bring in sea fog in these regions.

Forecasting Fog

Trying to forecast fog from your own observations of conditions is very difficult. One of the more positive ways to do this is to have a wet and dry bulb thermometer from which it is possible to establish the dew point of the ambient air, and if you have such a thermometer on board and are prepared to wave it around your head like a football rattle you can find out whether the dew point and the actual temperature are close, which would mean that there is a high risk of fog. However, you will get a good indication of whether fog is likely or not from the weather forecasts, and you will probably find that the forecasters will offer you either extensive fog or fog patches. If you are told that there is extensive fog, or widespread fog, then you can be pretty sure that you are going to be affected and you won't need to resort to your wet and dry bulb thermometer if you have such a thing. With extensive or widespread fog it is probably time to find a safe harbour or a quiet anchorage if you can, unless you are radar equipped, but even with radar you may not be able to cope with extensive fog.

With a forecast of extensive fog you are left in little doubt about the situation whilst with fog patches you may or may not be affected. In fog patches the fog may envelop you just when you are engaged in some critical navigation manoeuvre, and so the important thing here is to be able to try and identify what type of fog is being forecast, so you can have a better idea of where and how it might be expected and can plan a strategy accordingly.

Is it going to be Radiation Fog?
As we have already seen, radiation fog tends to occur in calm or near calm conditions. It requires clear night skies for this fog to form and you are unlikely to find this fog when the wind is blowing more than seven or eight knots. The conditions when radiation fog is likely are those associated with a high pressure area. If fog is forecast and these criteria can be met, particularly if it is spring or summer, then you can be reasonably sure that the fog being forecast is radiation fog. There may be an indication of this in the forecast which could specify coastal fog patches, and once again you can be fairly sure that these indicate radiation fog.

In the summer months there is a very good chance that radiation fog will burn off by mid-morning. The heat of the sun will rapidly raise the air temperature and prevent the water vapour from condensing. This means that there shouldn't be any need to forego a day's sailing if radiation fog is forecast. It is usually not too difficult to find your way out of harbour in fog, but it is finding your way back in which is the difficult part. The radiation fog is generally thickest just after dawn and then it should start to disperse – this dispersal is usually indicated initially by a watery sun shining through the fog and then gradually the fog will become patchy before finally disappearing. Often these conditions will herald a fine day and if you see these indications of dispersal then you can proceed to sea with a reasonable degree of confidence that you will have clear conditions out at sea. However the very conditions which promote this radiation fog are not likely to provide good sailing conditions, although they could be ideal for powerboat sailors. The fog may return again during the night but there is very little chance of this type of fog returning at least until darkness has fallen.

If you have established that it is radiation fog which is blanking out the visibility when you get up in the morning then it is sensible to wait until you see the signs of clearance before heading out to sea. Radiation fog can persist all day and even for a period of two or three days, and if the fog is going to clear then the signs of this will almost certainly occur during the

Extensive fog banks over the North Sea show up on this satellite picture and give forecasters the best indication of where fog occurs provided there is no cloud to hide it.

morning. If the fog still persists by midday then the chances of it clearing during that day are fairly remote, and you would be wise to delay departure until you get positive signs of clearance. If you are at sea and identify radiation fog as the type forecast then either stay reasonably well out at sea, perhaps up to ten miles from the coast where the chance of fog occurring will be very small, or alternatively plan your landfall for the afternoon or the evening when there is a good chance that the fog will have dispersed.

Is it going to be Advection Fog?

The conditions necessary for sea fog to form are not quite so easy to identify from the forecast charts or from a verbal forecast. However you can be reasonably positive that, if the forecasts give a wind of Force 3 or more and also forecast fog, they are talking about sea fog rather than radiation fog. The wind is an essential ingredient for the generation of sea fog, unlike radiation fog where it is the calm or near calm conditions which are the prerequisite. These winds may be blowing in from a southerly sector from the sea (in the northern hemisphere), but they could be blowing off a land mass which is warmer than the sea temperature, and this is likely to be the case if fog is forecast during the spring time. One of the important characteristics of sea fog is that it can extend over open sea conditions a long way from land and so you can be reasonably positive that any fog extending more than ten miles from the land will be sea fog.

Sea fog is much harder to cope with than radiation fog because it can last for two or three days and can be quite extensive in nature. Radiation fog can often be identified as a bank of fog on the horizon, but sea fog tends to arrive more gradually and it can also disperse more gradually so you are less likely to get the pleasant surprise of sailing out of a bank of fog into sunlight, which can happen with radiation fog. Sea fog can get patchy, particularly in fresh wind conditions when the turbulence can open up less dense patches of fog. The big problem with sea fog is trying to identify when it will occur, how long it will last, and when it will clear. Once you have identified that it is sea fog which is surrounding you, the weather forecasts are obviously going to be your best guide about the potential for clearance and what strategy you need to adopt in order to make a safe passage, or whether to hole up in an anchorage while the fog persists.

Visibility in Rain

Amongst the different types of rain which can affect visibility, drizzle is probably the one which creates the most extensive areas of poor visibility. The location of areas of potential drizzle can be identified from weather charts and are almost invariably associated with certain sections of depressions, as stated previously. Drizzle can also be a feature of the outer boundaries of an area of high pressure. High pressure areas are generally associated with fine weather and light winds, but these light winds whilst following the general circulatory pattern of the high pressure area, also flow slightly outwards from the centre, and the drizzle can occur where

SUMMARY OF FOG CHARACTERISTICS

Type of fog and season	Areas affected	Mode of formation	Mode of dispersal
Radiation fog (October to March)	Inland areas, especially low lying, moist ground	Cooling due to radiation from the ground on clear nights when the wind is light – is a feature of anti-cyclonic weather	Dispersed by the sun's radiation or by increased wind
Advection fog 1 Over land (Winter or Spring)	Often widespread in inland regions	Cooling of warm air by passage over cold ground, typical when warm air arrives after a cold spell	Increased wind produces a lift in the cloud base – the fog is dispersed by a change in air mass or the gradual warming of the ground
2 Over sea and coast-line (Spring and early Summer)	Sea and coasts adjacent, may penetrate for a few kilometres inland	Cooling of warmer air by passage over colder sea	Dispersed by a change in air mass – may be cleared over coast by the sun's heating
Frontal fog (At all seasons)	High ground	Lowering of the cloud base along the line of the front	Dispersed as the front moves and brings a change of air mass
Smoke fog or 'smog' (Winter)	Near industrial areas and large conurbations	Conditions for formation are similar to those for radiation fog	Dispersed by wind increase or by convection – is often slow to clear in stable anti-cyclonic air

these outward flowing winds come into contact with other air masses which will probably be towards the outer boundaries of low pressure areas. These can be mildly turbulent conditions which lead to the formation of drizzle, but trying to anticipate these conditions is very difficult and although the weather forecast will be your best guide, trying to pin down the actual areas where drizzle occurs is an imprecise part of the forecasting art.

Rain of all types will have its effect on visibility, and the heavy rain associated with thunderstorms and with the passage of the more virulent cold fronts can cut down visibility to half a mile or less. This type of rainfall tends to be fairly transient and is unlikely to last for much more than an hour, so if you find yourself in these heavy rainfall conditions just at the time when you are trying to make a landfall, then it is really just a question of being patient and waiting till the rain clears before attempting

POOR VISIBILITY

any tricky navigation. One of the biggest dangers of this heavy type of rainfall is that not only does it cut down visibility, but it can also affect the radar picture very considerably, making it impossible to pick out smaller targets such as buoys or small craft in these conditions. In heavy thunderstorms even large ships and areas of land can be difficult to identify on the radar, and although the loss of the radar may be transient it can cause serious navigation difficulties if you have been relying on this source of information. The more extensive rain associated with the passage of a warm front is not generally so heavy as that found in thunderstorms or cold fronts, but visibility in these conditions could come down to a mile and the rain could last for several hours. Though this type of rain does not generally impede safe navigation, you need to be more alert than normal because of the reduced visibility.

Trying to forecast poor visibility is notoriously difficult, partly because of the patchy nature of these conditions but also because of the variety of factors which can affect it. These can often be local in nature, but because the changes which can turn moderate visibility into poor visibility may often be very slight, it does not make it easy for the forecaster. You will obviously be able to see what your current visibility is and navigate accordingly and to a certain extent you can assess what lies ahead in terms of changes in visibility – but the weather forecast will always remain your best guide.

8 Weather Signs

Because of the ready availability of weather charts either from television or from weatherfax machines, and also the availability of general forecasts, we tend to concentrate more on what might be termed the 'global weather picture' these days than the local picture. Weather maps may cover the whole of the North Atlantic for instance and this gives us a broad general view of the weather patterns and their development, but such a view tends to ignore the local weather conditions and the significant information they can give. In many cases local weather conditions can provide indications of the progress of fronts and in some cases can even give early warning of changes. It is only by using these local weather signs in conjunction with the global picture that you can get a true feel for the overall weather situation and at the same time fine-tune it for your local position.

When it comes to 'seeing' the weather, clouds are one of the main indicators of what is happening to the weather systems. Fortunately there are a number of different types of cloud, each of which can give its own message about the weather. By being able to identify these different types of cloud and knowing how and why they are formed, it is possible to have a much better understanding of what the weather around you is doing.

The cloud forms seen in the sky reflect very clearly the physical processes which are taking place in the atmosphere, the heating and cooling and the air flows, and it is because of this that they can be excellent indicators of weather conditions. Except in certain cases which we will look at later, the clouds tell you what is happening now rather than foretelling the future; but this information is still valuable because the clouds can put a timing and location on the changes which are taking place.

How Clouds are Formed

To a certain extent, cloud formation is similar to fog formation in as much that clouds form when the air is cooled below its dew point. Thus when you get warm, moist air mixing with colder air, the colder air lowers the dew point of the moist, saturated air, the water vapour condenses and clouds are formed. The big difference between fog and cloud is that cloud is formed by contact between warm and cold air rather than warm air and cold land or sea. The clouds are generally formed because warm air is rising, and even though this rising air may be unsaturated initially, as it rises it becomes cooler and in becoming cooler it passes from the unsaturated to the saturated state at what is termed the condensation level. Any lowering of the temperature beyond this point results in the condensation of the excess water vapour to form clouds.

This is the simple explanation of cloud formation, and there are five main reasons which can cause the air flow to rise and initiate cloud formation. There is what is termed *orographic cloud*, which is formed when an air stream coming in from the sea is forced to rise over a coastline, hills or mountains where it cools and condenses. Then there is the air which rises owing to the surface heating by radiation from the sun. This is called '*thermal uplift*', when the air warmed by contact with the surface of the earth expands and becomes less dense than the surrounding air and so rises. The third cause of air rising comes through *turbulence* and this occurs mainly over an uneven land surface, although it could be found amongst islands where the uneven surface creates turbulence which causes air to rise. Although turbulence is generally a feature of low level rising air, it can also be found in higher altitudes, usually owing to conflicting air flows at these altitudes. The fourth cause of the air rising is termed *frontal uplift*. This is caused when warm air is overtaking cold air as in a frontal system and the warmer air rises over and above the cold air to create the familiar cloud formations of weather fronts. Finally there is the uplift resulting from *convergent winds*. We have seen how winds converge in the doldrums areas with the two sets of trade winds meeting in this region, and obviously if two air masses are flowing into one area, there is a surplus of air in this region and this surplus air is forced upwards. On a much smaller scale the same type of uplift can be found along coastlines where there is a convergence, and as well as increasing the strength of the wind in these areas this can also cause local uplift of the air.

Ten Types of Cloud

We have looked at these five different types of uplift in isolation but of course they can often occur in conjunction with each other, and the rise and fall of air flows, like most things associated with the weather, is rarely simple and straightforward. However, it is possible to identify specific types of cloud which in turn are related to different conditions; the four main types of cloud are:

1 *Cirrus*, a cloud which has a fibrous, feathery appearance;
2 *Cumulus*, a cloud having a peaked lump or towering; almost rock-like appearance with hard edges;
3 *Stratus*, clouds which appear to be in a fairly level sheet at a particular altitude; and
4 *Nimbus*, a ragged, low cloud, usually foretelling bad weather, and the type of cloud from which rain or snow usually emanates.

From these four basic types of cloud, meteorologists divide clouds up into ten different types, each of which has a particular significance in terms of weather conditions or changes, and particular types of cloud can be very useful to indicate what is going on in the atmosphere. Looking at the different cloud types, we will start from the lowest and work up. Sometimes the clouds span many thousands of feet of the atmosphere, so this height categorisation is only a rough guide, but it will help with the identification.

Stratus
This is a uniform layer of cloud which looks almost like a fog but doesn't rest on the ground. It is grey in colour, generally a fairly uniform light grey and is characterised by having no apparent structure. It will often envelop high ground which can give an indication of the height of the cloud base. A variation of stratus which has more character and form is fracto-stratus which is more broken and irregular. Both of these types of cloud can be quite thin and sometimes a weak, watery sun can be shining through the cloud. This type of cloud is generally associated with drizzle or poor visibility conditions and is often found in weak occlusions or at the tail end of warm or cold fronts.

Nimbostratus
This cloud is similar in many respects to stratus with a bottom layer between 500 and 2,000 feet high but it has much more body and apparent strength than stratus. It is usually a much darker grey and is commonly associated with continuous rain or snow. However rain or snow is not always present with this type of cloud because sometimes the precipitation associated with this cloud doesn't reach the ground – you can see the effect of this trailing precipitation as it gives a watery and ragged edge to the cloud. Often there can be low, ragged clouds lying beneath the main cloud layer, and these lower clouds or scud can be seen moving in relation to the higher clouds under the influence of strong surface winds. Nimbostratus cloud is usually associated with the passage of a warm front at the point where the front meets the sea, but in this situation the nimbostratus can be obscured by lower stratus cloud. The appearance of the nimbostratus cloud in this situation usually indicates that the front is clearing and that clearer, brighter weather can be expected as the nimbostratus passes overhead.

Stratocumulus
Stratocumulus cloud will often be found following behind the nimbostratus as the front passes. It is a less dense cloud than nimbostratus, with much shallower depth, although seen from sea level this cannot always be appreciated. It can be recognised by its softer, grey appearance with darker patches and its laminated or globular shapes which are often arranged in lines or in waves. Seen with the sun behind it stratocumulus can often seem to have very hard edges, and it is the cloud which often heralds the approach of the warm sector of a depression –

between the warm and cold fronts – and the better, brighter weather which is often found in this sector. In more dense form stratocumulus can cover the whole sky with no gaps, but even here lines or waves can be identified.

Cumulonimbus

This is the cloud which is primarily associated with a cold front, and it rises in mounting tiers with its base maybe only a thousand feet high, but its top over 30,000 feet high. The lower levels will seem a very dark grey and will often have rain coming from them, but higher up the cloud forms towering white or grey masses, particularly when the sun is shining on it. The base of a cumulonimbus cloud will often look like nimbostratus with the associated rain, and there can even be ragged clouds underneath the main layer. At the top of the cloud there will often be a characteristic handle shape as the cloud spreads out in higher wind – these anvil shaped tops are the result of strong convection currents within the cloud rising to high levels. Cumulonimbus clouds are often associated with very active weather frontal conditions and you can expect continuous heavy rain or heavy showers. Because of the associated cold fronts, there will often be a veering of the wind after the cumulonimbus cloud has passed through. The approach of this type of cloud may be hidden by lower clouds in front of it, but the presence of active showers will indicate that these clouds are present. These active clouds can produce hail as well as rain or snow and can sometimes result in thunderstorm conditions.

Cumulus

Cumulus clouds are rather like a less active version of cumulonimbus, but they tend not to extend so high up into the sky, often terminating at around 15,000 feet. They are clouds characteristic of the area of cold air behind the cold front and their strong, hard shape characterises the clear and improving conditions which are usually found in this area. Initially these cumulus clouds can produce showers, but if the cold front moves away the strength of the cumulus cloud tends to ease and the showers become less frequent. The size and shape of the cumulus cloud are a measure of its activity and the amount and weight of the showers which can be expected. This type is also called 'fair weather cumulus', when it is formed by similar upflowing air currents, but these occur over land owing to convection currents rising or to air lifting up over higher ground. This fair weather cumulus is rarely associated with rain or showers and is much lighter and fluffier in nature, hence its name. It can often indicate the presence of land when the land itself cannot be seen from sea level, but it is not necessarily a reliable guide for navigation.

Altostratus

Altostratus is a higher cloud usually found around the 15,000 feet mark. It is a fairly level and shallow cloud cover, sometimes quite heavy and dark and producing a watery sun through the weaker parts of the cloud.

Altostratus can appear in layers with the lower layers darker than the upper layers, and there is an element of threat in altostratus cloud partly because of its appearance and partly because it is one of the clouds which heralds the approach of a warm front and indicates that the rain associated with the front is about to start. Altostratus is the cloud which produces what is popularly known as a watery sky, and often the clouds will have a yellowish tinge particularly in the thinner parts of the otherwise fairly dense grey coverage.

Altocumulus

This is the cloud which will precede the altostratus as a warm front approaches. It is more patchy and lighter than the altostratus and is often arranged in regular layers or in lines or waves following one or two directions. This cloud tends to have thin and rather vague edges and a flattened appearance, and lacks much of the bulk of true cumulus. It tends to be a transition cloud merging on the one hand with altostratus at the lower levels, and at higher levels merging with the cirrostratus.

Cirrostratus

Cirrostratus cloud is rather like a veil of cloud, quite thin, allowing the sun or the moon to shine through it which can result in halos. In some cases it can have a white, almost milky appearance and in others it can have an apparently fibrous structure, and it can vary in density from nearly white cloud to quite grey. It will often cover the whole sky and is generally noted as being the herald of deteriorating weather, mainly because it indicates the approach of a warm front and the associated rain and winds which go with it. The associated halos are a further indication of the approach of the warm front particularly at night when the cloud type may not be clear. Cirrostratus is a high cloud often existing around the 30,000 foot mark, and its comparatively harmless appearance should never be trusted.

Cirrocumulus

This is what is popularly known as a 'mackerel sky', with small patches of fluffy cloud often arranged in groups or lines and often in quite regular patterns which can resemble the ripples of sand on the seashore. Cirrocumulus is really a transition cloud between the higher cirrus and the lower cirrostratus cloud and is often used as another message of worse weather to come, heralding the approach of a warm front.

Cirrus

This is probably the most easy cloud type to identify with its long, delicate strands of very high cloud, almost always white in colour, and often having a silky appearance. This is the highest cloud type of all, usually over 30,000 feet and it is composed almost entirely of ice crystals. These form in the region of the jet stream (see page 145) and it is these very strong winds at great height that often cause the delicate streaking characteristic of cirrus cloud. With this particular type of streaking, whether it is the 'mares' tails' or hooked shapes, these cirrus clouds have a number of messages for the local weather forecaster. In their broader sense, they are the first heralds of an approaching warm front, and their character can often be a guide to the intensity of the warm front and hence the depression from which the warm front is created. In this way cirrus clouds can be a very important tool for the local forecaster, particularly as the cloud is so easy to identify.

SUMMARY OF CLOUD CHARACTERISTICS

Name of cloud and usual abbreviation	Range of height of cloud base in Britain (metres)	Vertical thickness of cloud	Significant features
Cirrus (Ci)	6,000 to 12,000	Often a few hundred metres	Usually indicates an approaching frontal system
Cirrostratus (Cs)	6,000 to 12,000	Often a few hundred metres	Usually indicates an approaching frontal system – is accompanied by haloes round the sun
Cirrocumulus (Cc)	6,000 to 12,000	Fairly thin	—
Altocumulus (Ac)	2,000 to 6,000	A few hundred metres	Bands are often seen ahead of fronts – the castellated types are associated with thunder
Altostratus (As) (base often merges into nimbostratus)	2,000 to 6,000	Thick – may be up to 3,500 metres	Indicates closeness to precipitation area of frontal system
Nimbostratus (Ns)	100 to 600	Thick – may be up to 4,500 metres	Associated with precipitation – tops merge with altostratus
Stratus (St)	150 to 600	Thin – from 30 to 300 metres	May cover high ground
Stratocumulus (Sc)	300 to 1,350	Thin – from 150 to 900 metres	
Cumulus (Cu)	600 to 1,400	May be thick –1,400 to 4,500 metres	Is some indication of atmospheric stability – strong vertical currents in large types
Cumulonimbus (Cb)	600 to 1,400	Very thick – may be 300 to 9,000 metres	Very turbulent cloud, accompanied by heavy showers, perhaps of hail, lightning and thunder

Wind and Cloud

Clouds will move across the sky at the speed and direction of the wind at their own level. These winds at different levels are seldom constant which means that clouds at different heights can be moving in different directions at different speeds. Lower clouds will always seem to be moving faster than higher clouds simply because they are closer to the observer, and often it is very difficult to judge the speed and direction of the higher clouds, largely because there are few other clouds around with which to compare the apparent movement and also because of the distance of the cloud from the observer which makes them appear to be moving very slowly. Clouds are continually changing in form, and it is also important to remember that all an observer at sea level will see is often the lower base of the cloud, and that he cannot see what is going on above this. This is particularly the case with low, overcast skies where the structure of the cloud cannot be easily seen, and the first indication an observer will have of change is when either the rain stops or the low cloud starts to disperse allowing the higher clouds to come into view.

In order to appreciate fully the message from the clouds, it is not always the cloud type overhead which is important, because you know what weather it is giving since you are experiencing it at the time. What is much more important in trying to anticipate future weather is to watch the sequence of changes in the cloud system, how one type of cloud changes into another, how the cloud base rises or lowers, and the associated precipitation from these clouds. These are clues which can tell you a great deal about what is going on with the weather, and in order to analyse these in more detail we will look at the sequence of changes associated with the various frontal systems.

The Jet Stream

A warm front produces the most gradual and significant changes in cloud patterns to herald its arrival. The earliest indication of the arrival of the warm front is the jet stream, which is directly associated with the formation of depressions, and the arrival of cirrus clouds, sometimes called jet cirrus which are an indication of the turbulence going on in the vicinity of the jet stream. The jet stream tends to swing north and around the top of the centre of a depression in the northern hemisphere and then swing towards the south again ahead of the depression. The cirrus cloud associated with the jet stream can thus give you early warning of the approach of the depression and the associated warm front.

The warm front itself is made up of warm air rising over and above a mass of cold air and this frontal line between the cold and warm air can rise to 30,000 or 40,000 feet. It is the warm air which has a relatively high level of water vapour, and is first indicated by the delicate cirrus clouds. These cirrus clouds will often have a hooked appearance as they feel the effects of the jet stream ahead. The fine wispy clouds appear to follow an apparently straight line and then the ends of the cloud are hooked slightly upwards. It is the hooks at the end of the straight clouds, fairly sharp and almost turning back on themselves which indicate the maximum wind sheer between the rising warm air and the jet stream. This can be an indication that the jet stream is not very far away and is located on the polar, that is the northern side in the northern hemisphere, of the cirrus clouds. In more active weather situations the activity in the cirrus clouds becomes more intense and it is possible to get great dense streaks of cirrus clouds across the horizon, which can be an indication of severe weather conditions to follow.

The main element here is to try and judge the speed of these cirrus clouds because it is the speed at which they are travelling which gives an indication of the strength of the jet stream which in turn gives a clue to the intensity of the approaching depression. Because of their height it is not easy to judge the speed of the cirrus cloud and often the clouds will appear to be stationary. The best criterion to follow here is that if you can actually see the cirrus cloud moving, then you know it is travelling at 100 knots or more and you can expect a fairly active depression as a result. It is in the winter months that the jet stream tends to be particularly active and sometimes in these conditions you can see the cirrus cloud moving across the sky quite rapidly which indicates that the jet stream is nearing its maximum speed of close to 200 knots. The stronger the jet stream the more active the weather associated with it tends to be. This is because the speed of the jet stream will increase when there is a larger difference in temperature between the cold and the warm air masses involved in the weather patterns. This larger difference in temperature between the warm and cold air masses also tends to be associated with deeper and more intense depressions and more active fronts, and so you can expect to find stronger winds and sharper changes in wind direction when you can actually see these cirrus clouds moving quickly across the sky.

Depression Approaching
At the point when you see the cirrus cloud developing there is unlikely to be a positive indication of much change from the barometer readings which you take on board. The drop in readings from the approaching depression will not be noticeable yet so the cirrus can give valuable early warning. The behaviour of the barometer readings will depend on the track of the depression in relation to your location and the warning signs given by the high cirrus will tell you where the centre of the depression is located. One way you can establish roughly the direction of the centre is to use Buys-Ballot's Law. In the northern hemisphere, if you stand with your back to the direction of the wind then the centre of the depression will be located on your left hand side. This means that with a south easterly wind, which is often the direction of the wind in the early part of an approaching depression which is passing to the north of you, Buys-Ballot's Law will indicate that the centre of the depression lies to the north west of you. If you find that the wind is from the south, then by using this rule you can see that the depression is to the west of you – and this could indicate that you are on or near the direct path of the centre of the depression as it will

tend to move in a west to east direction, at least in the north Atlantic. (Where directions are mentioned, they refer to the development of depressions in the northern hemisphere. The diagrams show how everything is reversed in the southern hemisphere.)

Buys-Ballot's Law: with the wind behind you the low pressure will be on your left hand side and high pressure on the right, in the northern hemisphere.

If you are in the direct path of the centre of the depression you will see a significant drop taking place in the barometer readings and this can give you a further clue to the location of the centre of the depression, whereas if you are to the north east or south east of the centre, the barometer is likely to be more erratic and the drop in pressure much less rapid.

Warm Front

With most depressions it is the southern sector which is of particular interest because this is where the strongest winds often lie and it is the sector more likely to affect yachts sailing in temperate climates where the depressions tend to move away towards the north. Here it is the approaching cirrus clouds which will probably give you your first indication of the approaching warm front, and these cirrus clouds could be seen anything up to 500 miles from the actual warm front. This will be the sort of distance involved with a well developed depression, but with smaller, developing depressions this distance could be as short as 200 or 300 miles. The more severe the depression the earlier the warning you are likely to get from the high cirrus cloud.

From this point on, the cirrus cloud will be overtaken firstly by possibly a mackerel sky but certainly by cirrostratus, then altostratus, followed by the heavy nimbostratus cloud which indicates the actual passage of the front. The rain is likely to start when the altostratus cloud gets overhead, which could be up to 300 miles in advance of the front with a well developed depression and frontal system. This rain will start off as very light and intermittent and gradually increase in strength to form continuous heavy rain at the surface front.

As you get closer to the more intense parts of the front, usually where the rain starts, the wind will often freshen and you will see the barometer start to fall more rapidly. A lot will depend on how intense the depression

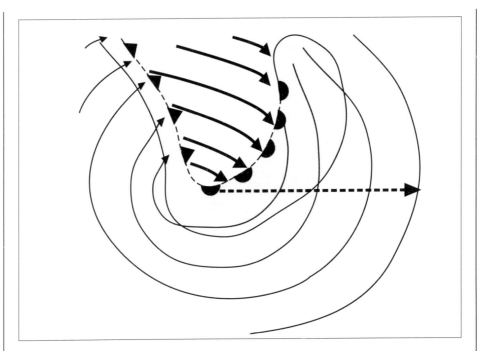

Above: a typical northern hemisphere depression with the shaded section showing the main rain areas and the broken arrow showing the direction of travel. The stronger arrows denote the warm air section of the depression.
Below: a typical southern hemisphere depression where the circulation is reversed.

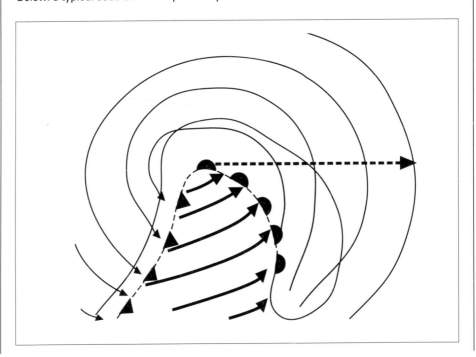

associated with the fronts is as to how strong the wind gets and how much the barometer falls. This increased activity is indicated by the way in which the isobar lines often come together more tightly close to this point. The line of the front is actually a trough in the isobars and this trough represents something like a valley which tends to concentrate the wind more in this point.

A heavy and well defined line squall approaching as part of an active cold front.

When the front goes through you will see this by the fact that the barometer tends to steady up and the wind either eases or stops altogether. Probably the best indication you will get is the fact that the wind will swing round probably through thirty to sixty degrees so that if it has been south westerly before the front, you can expect westerly winds after the front. Now we are entering what is called the warm sector of the depression and if you have been keeping an eye on your thermometer then you should see a rise in temperature of a few degrees reflecting the warmer air you are entering. Cloud cover can vary a great deal in this warm sector, but because the air tends to be warmer and moister it provides an active breeding ground for cloud which could be mainly low stratus or stratocumulus. The heavy continuous rain of the front will have stopped but it could be replaced by drizzle. Visibility will tend to be moderate or poor, and if there is cold land or sea in the path of the warm air then fog is a possibility. This will be sea fog because the winds are likely to be still quite fresh in this sector.

The weather you find in this warm sector will depend a great deal on how close you are to the centre of the depression. Within a couple of hundred miles of the centre of a large depression you are probably not going to see a lot of change in the weather conditions as the front goes through and the rain will remain more or less continuous although it could take the form of a heavy drizzle rather than the heavy downpour at the front itself. Because of the almost continuous cloud you won't see much change in the cloud structure as seen from sea level, and the main indication will once again be the change in wind direction with the wind veering as you enter the warm sector. The further you are from the centre the better the conditions and generally the lighter the winds. Even though you have experienced the rain and the change in the wind as the front went through, you may experience quite moderate conditions after the front has gone through, if you are a long way from the centre of the depression, because here the isobars tend to get more spaced out giving lighter winds and much less cloud.

SUMMARY OF WARM FRONT CHARACTERISTICS

Element	In advance	At the front	In the rear
Pressure	Steady fall	Fall ceases	Little change
Wind	Backs and increases	Veers and decreases	Steady
Temperature	Steady or slow rise	Rises slowly	Little change
Humidity	Gradual increase	Rapid rise	Little change
Cloud	Ci, Cs, As, Ns in succession	Low nimbostratus and fractostratus	Stratus and stratocumulus
Weather	Continuous rain (or snow in winter)	Precipitation almost stops	Fair conditions or intermittent slight rain or drizzle
Visibility	Good, except in rain	Poor – mist and low cloud produce poor visibility	Often poor, with low cloud and mist or fog

This table, and the one following on page 152, provide a useful guide to the weather signs of an approaching and passing depression. With practice, a yacht skipper can recognise these signs, build them in to his view of the prevailing weather pattern, and then make passage planning decisions. A good 'feel' for the weather can make all the difference between enjoyable sailing, and battling against the elements.

Cold Front

Still to come in this sequence of weather from the depression is the cold front, and this is generally the most active part of the depression. In theory you should be able to see the cold front coming because of its high towering cumulonimbus clouds. Whereas the warm front was at quite a shallow angle, so that the clouds extended over a large sea area, the cold front is a nearly vertical division between the warm air in front and the cold air behind and it is this which is responsible for the high towering clouds. However, quite often the cumulonimbus will be obscured by the stratus cloud of the warm sector. In this case the first indication that the cold front is approaching will be the start of heavy, continuous rain, the rain activity generally depending on how active the front is. This rain can be very heavy and concentrated in an active front. It will generally start with little warning and as the front passes the continuous rain will tend to become squally. This is usually a sign that the worst of the front is past and in one of the more active of these squalls the wind will probably settle down to a new direction which could be as much as 90 degrees from the original. More normally the wind will veer through 45 degrees or so and this change will tell you that the rain will stop shortly and you will enter the showery conditions typical of the aftermath of the passage of a cold front. Now the barometer will start to rise after being more or less steady in the warm sector. The temperature may drop a few degrees and you will find more patchy cumulus clouds, although in the more active cold front, this could be cumulonimbus bringing quite heavy showers. The sky colour is characterised by a hard, often duck egg blue colour, which tells you that the worst of the depression is now over and you should be able to look forward to improving conditions with clearing skies and reducing wind.

What Else You May Experience

This is a typical sequence of weather that you can expect from the passage of a depression which is to the north of you in the northern hemisphere, or to the south of you in the southern hemisphere. If you are positioned so that the centre of the depression passes over or close to you the sequence of change will be different, with almost continuous rain during the passage of the depression. The changes in wind direction will tend to be more sudden and concentrated near the centre of the depression and as this centre passes, the wind can become quite light before freshening from a new direction. A swing in wind direction through 180 degrees can take place within an hour or two.

If the centre of the depression passes to the south of you in the northern hemisphere then you will probably escape the frontal systems associated with the depression and instead experience a steady change in the wind direction as it backs round. Within 200 miles of the centre of the depression you will probably experience a long spell of continuous rain but you will probably escape the more violent changes and activity associated with the southern sector of the depression.

We are discussing here the pattern of a typical depression, but you have to bear in mind that depressions come in all sorts of shapes and sizes and there is no guarantee that this sequence of events is going to be followed. Depressions can be oval rather than round in shape causing sharper and more sudden changes of wind direction in the fronts. Another depression may be following close behind, and then the wind changes after the cold front has passed will not be as expected. There can even be two centres to a depression where two low pressure areas are amalgamating.

SUMMARY OF COLD FRONT CHARACTERISTICS

Element	In advance	At the front	In the rear
Pressure	Falls	Sudden rise	Slow continuous rise
Wind	Backs and increases	Veers suddenly – often accompanied by line squalls – ie severe winds along frontal boundary	Slow backing, after squall then steady
Temperature	Steady – sometimes a slight fall in rain	Sudden fall	Little change
Humidity	No great change	Sudden fall	Generally low
Cloud	Altocumulus and altostratus, followed by cumulonimbus	Cumulonimbus with fractocumulus or low nimbostratus	Lifts rapidly, but cumulus or cumulonimbus may develop
Weather	Some rain, with possible thunder	Heavy rain often accompanied by hail and thunder	Heavy rain for a short period – fine spell – followed by further showers
Visibility	Poor – some fog	temporary deterioration – rapid improvement	Very good

Occluded Front

One factor which can have a considerable impact on the weather associated with the passage of a depression is whether the warm and cold fronts have joined together in what is called an occlusion. This tends to happen initially towards the centre of the depression where the cold air behind has caught up with the cold air in front and pushed the warm air upwards away from the surface. There are two types of occlusion, a warm front occlusion where the overtaking air is cold, but not so cold as the air which has been ahead of the front. This type of occlusion will not be as active as the cold front occlusion where the colder air is coming up behind and overtaking the cooler air in front. This cold air occlusion is the more common type found in Atlantic and European areas, but as far as the weather is concerned, you will probably not notice a great deal of difference between the two types. The weather found in an occlusion is somewhat like that found in a cold front. It tends to be comparatively localised with moderate to heavy rain coming down from the clouds contained in the raised warm air, and the main difference between the two will be the height of the cloud base which will tend to be higher in the occlusion because the mixing of warm and cold air takes place away from the sea surface. You are unlikely to get any of the squalls or other activity found in the cold front and the change in the barometer readings will only be slight as the occlusion passes through, but you should still get the characteristic veering of the wind and the brightening up of the weather after the front has passed.

The length of the occluded front out from the centre tends to vary with the age of the depression. The older the depression, the more time the fronts have had to become occluded. In general warm fronts tend to move forwards at around fifteen knots, whereas cold fronts tend to move at around twenty knots and this explains why one will catch up with the other. The depressions themselves may move at twenty to thirty knots as an average speed, but can move as fast as fifty knots, particularly if they are small and intense. Larger depressions tend to move more slowly but almost invariably the depression itself is moving faster than the frontal systems associated with it, which explains why these fronts gradually curl round, become occluded and then trail off to the west as the depression moves to the east.

It is these long tails which can be either a cold front or an extended occluded front or a mixture of both which can cause havoc with your local weather forecasting. With the depression moving to the east, these long tails of cold or occluded fronts will often stretch out a long way to the west and if you happen to be around the same latitude, then you could get stuck in a long period of rain which would seem inexplicable in terms of the normal weather patterns you would expect from a depression. When the trailing fronts get to this stage they have probably lost a considerable amount of their activity and it is usually an indication that the depression is failing and dying, but that is small consolation if you are stuck in this band of continuous drizzle or light rain which doesn't seem to form part of the normal pattern of depression weather. This is where having a weather map can be vital to understanding the local weather and local changes which are taking place.

Cloud Observation

You can understand a great deal about the changing weather patterns from local observations of the clouds, rain and winds and the changes in the barometer readings. However local analysis does tend to be found wanting when depressions take up strange shapes or when their behaviour is different from the regular pattern, or perhaps when secondary lows develop along frontal systems, and this is where the weather map plays a vital role as a secondary source of information. What these local changes in the weather do is enable you to put a much closer timing on the weather forecast. For instance, if you know when the rain started at the advance of a warm front, and you know the speed of advance of that front from the weather map, then you can predict more accurately when the rain will stop and the wind will veer, always assuming that the front follows the normal pattern, which the forecast maps will confirm. In a similar way the rain and cloud changes will enable you to put a more accurate timing on the wind veering with the passage of the cold front.

What you have to remember when making these assessments from changes in local weather is that you are mainly interested in the wind strength and direction, and particularly when the strength increases or the direction changes. This is the information you can get from watching cloud changes, from the indications of rain starting and stopping, or being heavier or lighter and from the changes in the barometer readings. These are all clues which can let you know what the wind is likely to do and it is the wind which rules your life at sea.

Weather Lore

Before the advent of the sophisticated weather forecasting systems that we have today, seamen had to be much more aware of the weather and be capable of making their own forecasts from the weather signs which were available to them, simply by looking at the sky. Their sense of change from these local signs was much more finely tuned because it was their sole source of weather information, and they came up with a lot of weather sayings, some of which may have had local application, others more general application.

One of the most popular of these weather sayings is 'Long foretold – long last, short notice – soon past'. This relates to the size of a depression and suggests that if you get early warning such as with a steadily falling barometer or high cirrus cloud long before the weather starts to change, then you are in for a long period of changeable weather, whereas short, rapid variations in pressure and in cloud patterns tend to indicate a fast moving depression. Another saying which also relates to the advancing cirrus cloud is, 'Mackerel sky and mares' tails, make lofty ships carry low sails'. This suggests that when you see these high cirrus clouds you have some stronger winds coming towards you, which would certainly be the case with an advancing warm front. Another saying relating to the advance of a depression is, 'When the wind backs and the weather glass falls, then be on your guard against gales and squalls'. This is again the type of conditions you can get with an approaching depression.

Another favourite saying is 'Rain before seven, fine before eleven', which is simply reinforcing the fact that rain rarely lasts for more than four hours at a time, although there is a degree of optimism in this saying because periods of lighter rain can certainly last longer than the four hours, particularly if you happen to be caught along the line of a frontal system rather than one which passes quickly through your position. Such a saying is not particularly significant in terms of time, because it could equally happen that the rain starts at midday and could be over by four o'clock. The seven and eleven were probably chosen simply to cheer up people who woke up to rain that morning, that there could be an improvement coming along.

Your Own Observations

These old sayings about the weather certainly have a strong element of truth in them, but again they only tell part of the story and have to be related to close observation of what the cloud formations are doing and how the weather patterns in general are changing. Gradually things have become more scientific for the single station observer, and the barometer readings certainly can give you a more positive clue about what is going on in terms of changes in the weather. The barometer readings will help you to identify approaching depressions not so much by the readings themselves but by the rate at which the barometer is falling. This will also give you a clue as to the intensity of the depression and you should be able to identify the passage of the warm and cold fronts from the barometer readings. Like observations of the clouds, the barometer readings don't tell the full story, but in conjunction with the messages from the clouds and the rain, you can build up a more comprehensive picture. Another part of this approach should be to use Buys-Ballot's Law which can tell you approximately the direction in which the centre of the depression lies. Knowing where the centre of the depression is in relation to your position, and the likely pattern of frontal systems which emanate from this centre, you probably have enough information from which to start making positive decisions about your future strategy.

From these observations you should be able to build up quite a good mental picture of the general weather pattern, certainly as far as depressions are concerned, for they are the features which are going to create the major weather changes. It is rather like detective work, putting all these clues together, knowing where the centre of the depression is, where the frontal systems are, and matching the cloud signs for indication and confirmation of these changes – and now you have most of the ingredients in place to make reasonably accurate forecasts. One of the sad things with modern weather forecasts is that yachtsmen have become very lazy and tend to rely on what the forecast says rather than making their own observations. The two go hand in hand.

Making your own observations and taking barometer readings every couple of hours can help to confirm how the forecast is changing, but perhaps more importantly it enables you to put a much more accurate timing on the forecast changes. When the forecast says the wind is going

WEATHER SIGNS

to veer to the north west, this probably means that it will change after a cold front has passed through. From your observations you will have a pretty good idea from the cloud formations and the rain about the approaching cold front and now you can pinpoint accurately when the wind will change. It is the same with an approaching warm front, and with the clues available you should be able to pinpoint accurately when the wind will change. That high cirrus cloud will give you early warning, usually plenty of time to seek shelter or plan a strategy to cope with the freshening winds ahead.

It is easy to ignore these observed changes and stick with what the weather forecast says. Reading the message in the clouds and in the weather in general sounds old-fashioned and unscientific in a modern world which can produce satellite pictures of the weather from the other side, but these observations still have a very positive value, as any meteorologist will tell you.

9 Extremes of Weather

The last chapter demonstrated how you can get a better appreciation of the weather by combining local observation with the forecast information. However there are some weather conditions which tend to be comparatively local and may not show up on the weather forecast, and these you can only deduce from local observation. Some of these phenomena such as thunderstorms and waterspouts can be very local indeed and as well as the difficulty of forecasting where they will occur, it is also very hard to forecast the specific conditions necessary for these phenomena to start, although the forecast may indicate that there is a general risk. This is why observation of what is going on around you is so important and will give you at least some warning of these local, often violent phenomena. Other phenomena such as hurricanes and cyclones, whilst not necessarily easy to forecast, have such a destructive power that weather watchers search avidly for the first signs of their formation so that they can be tracked and warnings issued. The chances of being overtaken by hurricanes or cyclones without warning these days is comparatively small, but if you sail in the areas where they are common you could find yourself one day without a working radio and thus the means to obtain warnings, so recognising the signs by visual observation can be important. Even if you have the radio warning, recognising the approaching signs can help to put a much more accurate timing on the warning.

Signs of a Thunderstorm

Probably the most frequent of these extreme weather phenomena are thunderstorms, and these are found in most parts of the world frequented by yachts. They can be very local but very intense, and consist of a mass of turbulent air which at the surface can produce wind speeds of fifty or sixty knots in the more active thunderstorms. Whilst the possibility of thunderstorms can be forecast in general terms, the specific location of any such storm can only be observed visually. If you can recognise the signs you can have adequate warning of the onslaught, and possibly take avoiding action.

Whilst there are two main types of thunderstorm, they have similar characteristics. The main danger signal which warns of an approaching thunderstorm is a large cumulus cloud which grows rapidly. From this

EXTREMES OF WEATHER

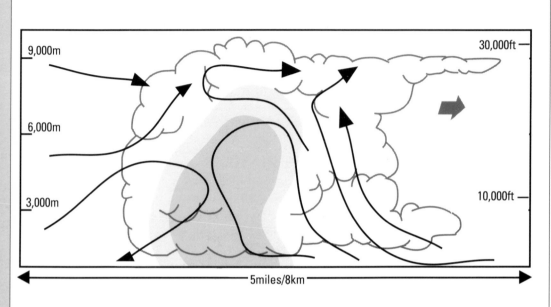

A cross section through a typical thunderstorm showing the wind flow and areas of heavy rain or hail. The roll cloud at the lower leading edge of the thunderstorm is where some of the more intense activity can occur.

cumulus cloud, a large characteristic anvil shaped cloud will grow out of the top, whilst underneath the cloud it will get darker and it may already be possible to see the heavy rain which is a feature of a thunderstorm. There are four distinct features in every thunderstorm cloud although these may not always be visible, because other clouds may prevent you seeing the complete cloud formation. At the top there is the characteristic anvil shaped cloud which is composed of cirrus, and this can reach up to 30,000 feet or more. This top anvil cloud tends to point in the direction in which the upper wind is blowing. This same direction also tells us which way the storm is moving which can be different from the surface wind. Watching this anvil cloud is an important feature if you are thinking about taking avoiding action because you will obviously sail away from the direction in which it is pointing. However, depending on which way you are viewing the cloud, it is not always easy to get a clear picture of which way this cloud is pointing.

Next there is the main body of the cloud, a huge billowing cumulus cloud which can extend up to 20,000 feet and has the appearance of intense activity, although the actual cloud moves in comparatively slow motion. Then there is the roll cloud which is formed by violent air currents along the leading edge of the base of the cumulus cloud. This is probably the area containing the most intense activity because this is where the main updraught of air comes into the cloud. There is considerable turbulence in this leading edge which often extends out from the main body of the cumulus cloud. The turbulence is exaggerated here because the thunderstorm tends to move in a different direction to the surface wind. Finally, of the four thunderstorm features, there is the dark area under the cloud which usually extends down to water level and encompasses the heavy rain which is typical of thunderstorms, although at the edges there could be hail as well as rain.

If these visual features were not adequate warning of an approaching thunderstorm then there is the noise of the thunder and the flash of the lightning. However by the time you hear or see these the storm may be too close to take any avoiding action – the visual features already listed are likely to be the ones which help you identify the thunderstorm in the first place.

Of the two main types of thunderstorm, heat thunderstorms are those which tend to rely on solar heating of the land to initiate the violent air movements which get the thunderstorm moving. The second type is the frontal thunderstorm which tends to be mainly associated with very active cold front conditions.

Heat Thunderstorms

Heat thunderstorms are generally found in summer when the layers of air in contact with the ground become heated sufficiently to produce rapid convection currents. The column of quickly rising, heated air which is generated from the solar heating of the land causes air to flow in from all sides to replace the rising air. This air flowing into the base of the embryo thunderstorm should be warm and moist for the thunderstorm to develop. Thunderstorms of this type are more frequent in the summer months and particularly occur during the afternoon or early evening when the land has become well heated by the daytime sun. They normally occur in light wind conditions when the air is not circulating over the land. They can be found particularly in cols, the ridges between high and low pressure areas, or in association with very shallow depressions, both conditions which produce the required light winds.

These heat thunderstorms tend to be local in nature and form in a random way, initially almost invariably over land where the heating from the sun is sufficient to generate the rapidly rising column of air. The sultry, still air often associated with these conditions is a recognisable feature which creates the saying that 'a thunderstorm is needed to clear the air'. Thunderstorms of this type tend to be found only in coastal waters where they have started over land and then drifted out to sea. They can be a feature of more enclosed areas of water such as the English Channel. In the USA thunderstorms are more frequent in the south eastern part of the country owing to the intense heating of the land, and again only affect yachts when they drift out to sea or extend over harbour or estuary areas.

Frontal Thunderstorms

A frontal thunderstorm is a different animal altogether and tends to be associated with very active cold fronts. Here you can get rapidly rising air currents because the cold air from the cold sector is pushing forwards and under the warm air causing this warm air to rise. In a very active front this warm air can rise quickly, and the situation becomes intensified if there is a considerable difference in temperature between the air in the cold and warm sectors. It will also be more active if the angle between the winds in the tail end of the warm sector and the front of the cold sector is considerable, perhaps approaching 90 degrees. Cold front thunderstorms can occur in a series of storms sometimes closely linked together along the line of the front. This means that if the front is passing across your location you may experience only one thunderstorm, but if it is passing along your position then you could be in for a series of thunderstorms one after the other, which would appear to merge into one long thunderstorm. Unlike the heat thunderstorms, frontal thunderstorms tend to be more frequent in the winter months, simply because there are more depressions and hence cold fronts at this time, and they tend to be more frequent out at sea than on land.

Thunderstorms can also be associated with warm fronts when these are particularly active but because the angle of ascent of the warm air is comparatively shallow at these fronts, thunderstorms will only occur if there is sufficient energy and activity in the air flow to cause the rapid upward air currents which are necessary. Even then it may only be thunder and lightning which gives you a clue that there is a thunderstorm in a warm front. The heavy rain which is a characteristic of both thunderstorms and warm fronts will be much the same, and the low clouds of the warm front will mask the characteristic cloud formations of the thunderstorm.

Thunderstorms can also occur with occluded fronts and even though the occlusions may seem to be comparatively weak and harmless they can develop into surprisingly active fronts, especially when they are passing from sea to land. Such thunderstorms occur mainly in the summer.

Although thunderstorms can occur both day and night they tend to be more frequent in the late afternoon or early evening, particularly in inland or coastal waters. This is when the land has had the maximum time to heat up and initiate the strong convection currents. Over the ocean, thunderstorms tend to be more frequent between midnight and sunrise and here the most frequent and violent thunderstorms will be found in sub-tropical latitudes.

Passage of a Thunderstorm

Ahead of the thunderstorm the wind will be steady if it is a frontal thunderstorm, or light and variable if it is a heat storm. As the roll cloud at the lower edge of the advancing storm comes closer, the wind will tend to weaken and become variable, but then as the roll cloud passes overhead you can expect to find violent winds coming from various directions, often accompanied by strong downdraughts. This is an area of considerable turbulence and here the wind can reach speeds of sixty knots or more. Just behind this violent wind you can expect to find heavy rain, or sometimes hail.

The violence of an approaching thunderstorm can often be gauged by the height of the towering clouds. The anvil top of the cloud stretches up into the jet stream which is why it takes on its characteristic shape and develops rapidly. If this anvil is over 30,000 feet high then you can expect the storm to be violent. Less violent thunderstorms only reach up to 20,000 feet or so, and these are the type often found in the spring or autumn. There is no easy way to judge the height of the cloud except to say that if the anvil top is missing or very poorly developed, then this will usually indicate that the top of the cloud is lower and conditions will tend to be less severe. A feature identified in some of the more severe thunderstorms is what is called a microburst. Although most of the air is being drawn up into the thunder cloud, the violent turbulence inside the cloud leads to dense columns of sinking air which come down from the cloud and spread out in all directions when they hit the surface. Winds of up to 120 knots have been measured in some of these microbursts – they may last only for a few minutes but can be devastatingly strong as far as yachts are concerned. Fortunately the effect is confined to strong winds because the sea does not have any time to generate the sort of wave conditions normally associated with such strong winds.

The rain will tend not to fall continuously during a thunderstorm, but usually in very heavy showers. The primary rain area is after the roll cloud has passed over and usually follows after the first bursts of very strong

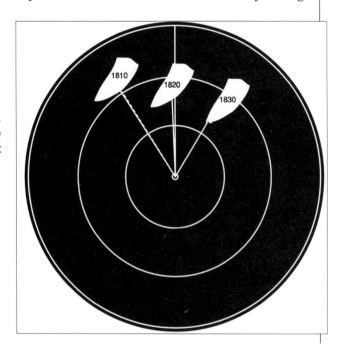

Thunderstorms and heavy showers show up well on radar and the radar can be used to plot avoiding action. The technique of putting the bearing cursor on the target will show how it is moving and in this case an alteration to port would be the best avoiding action.

winds. Often the rain will cease and then start again with considerable strength after a lightning flash. This rain usually starts off as large drops and changes to smaller drops with the passage of time. The lightning which is a feature of thunderstorms can be quite frightening when it is in close proximity, and the peals of thunder which follow it add to the general feelings of threat and tension which are associated with thunderstorms. If you can count the seconds between the flash of lightning and the noise of the thunder, and then divide this number of seconds by five, it will give you an approximate distance off in statute miles. However, by the time you can see and hear the lightning and thunder you should be close enough to see the storm anyway, although this could be a useful guide at night time. Radar can also give you early warning of a thunderstorm approaching as the storm itself will make a very strong target on the radar. You should be able to pick the storm up twenty miles away or more and you will be able to plot its progress quite accurately, enabling you to take avoiding action in good time, provided that this is an isolated thunderstorm and not one of a series. Another guide to approaching thunderstorms is the static which will appear on any MF or AM radio.

Thunderstorms should not be taken lightly because of the severe winds which can be found within them. The risk of being struck by lightning is quite small and because of the surrounding water the main damage likely to result from a lightning strike is to the electrical or electronic equipment on the boat rather than the structure itself, particularly if the yacht has a metal mast. However the violence of thunderstorms should serve as a warning of the possibility of very strong winds of limited duration which can occur with little warning.

Line Squalls

Line squalls, like some thunderstorms, are generally associated with the passage of a cold front. Indeed a line squall could be considered as a very direct and positive manifestation of the line of a cold front producing visual evidence of the change from warm to cold air and the turbulence at the violent interface.

You can't mistake a line squall with its line of dark grey, almost black cloud extending from horizon to horizon. This line of cloud is usually very clearly defined and can often have the appearance of an arch across the sky with a watery, hazy look across the black arch. This is the main warning sign that you will soon get turbulent wind conditions. Once you are close to or under the line squall then there can be a whole sequence of events. The wind speed can rise very rapidly, often with squall-like suddenness, and at the same time there can be a considerable change in wind direction. For sailboats this can be quite a devastating experience, and if you have time to look at the instruments you will find that there has been a rapid drop in temperature of several degrees and probably a rapid rise in the barometer. Just to add to the misery of the line squall there is usually heavy rain, sometimes hail and quite often thunder and lightning.

EXTREMES OF WEATHER

Force 12 North Atlantic. In extreme winds the sea has a frightening random effect with heavily breaking waves which present extreme danger to small craft

A line squall will tend to follow the line of the cold front associated with a depression. This storm front or line squall front will move in from the west or perhaps the north west. The line of dark, almost black cloud will have passed overhead before the rain actually starts. The wind, which may have been the steady breeze often found in the warm front sector of a depression, will often fall light just before the line squall is overhead with the winds from the south or south west. When the strong or violent winds associated with the line squall start they will usually be from a west or north west direction; this squall usually starts just when the dark cloud is overhead and ends when the heavy rain starts.

Line squalls tend to travel from west to east following the same trend as cold fronts and usually they are too extensive to enable you to take avoiding action. However, they are not usually uniform along their length and often you will be able to see light patches along a dark line of a squall. These lighter patches indicate reduced activity and these are the areas to head for if you want to get as smooth a passage as possible through the line squall. You may be able to identify the less dense patches of the line squall on the radar, and this may also be a help in trying to plot a course towards the areas of weaker activity. Line squalls, like thunderstorms, are not something to be taken lightly and whilst you still want to maintain steerage way on a sailboat, you certainly want to have the sail area reduced before the squall or thunderstorm hits. The heavy rain in both line squalls and thunderstorms can cut down visibility quite severely, perhaps to a quarter of a mile or less, and the combination of poor visibility and strong, sometimes violent winds produces very trying conditions, which however normally last for no longer than half an hour before some sort of normality returns.

Waterspouts

The violent conditions which generate both thunderstorms and line squalls can also create a much rarer phenomenon, the waterspout. Waterspouts are the marine equivalent of the tornado which is one of the most violent winds found anywhere in the world. The tornado tends to be found mainly in the USA and Australia and is usually associated with a well marked cold front or the boundary between two air masses of widely differing temperatures. The waterspout is the ocean equivalent, but is generally much less violent and usually associated with either line squalls or the characteristic cumulonimbus cloud of the cold front. They are found much more frequently in warm tropical waters than they are in temperate climates, but waterspouts have been seen in areas such as the Thames estuary and the English Channel.

The sort of cloud which can produce waterspouts is the very black thunderstorm or line squall type of cloud, though this black cloud may well appear without there being visible rain descending from it. Instead there may be what is known as 'mammae' which look rather like cow's teats hanging down below the cloud at intervals and visibly moving or swaying. A 'mammae' appears to be the embryo waterspout and as you watch, one or more of them will change into the characteristic funnel shaped cloud which gradually extends down towards the sea beneath. Some waterspouts may not reach the sea surface but appear to remain suspended from the clouds, whilst those that do extend down to the sea will throw up spray and cause a very locally agitated area of sea around the base of the waterspout. The waterspout does not usually descend vertically but will often adopt quite a curve, particularly at the top end where it descends from the cloud. Once fully formed the waterspout will advance with the cloud and it may last anything from five minutes to half an hour before it becomes unstable, when it will appear to break well above the sea surface and rapidly disperse.

Waterspouts normally descend from clouds which are round about 1,000 feet above the sea surface and they are usually very slim. The diameter of the waterspout can be as small as 20 feet, or as large as 200 feet in diameter where it touches the water. There is considerably reduced air pressure in the centre of this base area which causes the sea to rise around this contact point, although this rise will be largely hidden by the amount of spray which is flying around. For yachts both power and sail, waterspouts are something to be avoided because winds within the spout can be up to 100mph. The waterspout probably travels at around about 20mph and it shouldn't be too difficult to take avoiding action, although the movement of the waterspout where it contacts the water can be rather erratic. The best solution is to give the waterspout as wide a berth as possible, even turning around and running away from it, but there can be difficulties in this if you are in narrow channels. If it looks as though you are going to have a close encounter with a waterspout then make sure you get all the sails down and stowed, and all openings closed off and make sure all the crew are inside the boat under cover.

Where Hurricanes are Likely

In contrast with the very localised but quite violent effects of the waterspout the hurricane is a major threat. Its effects can be felt over hundreds of miles of sea and its life can extend for several days during which it can cover enormous distances. Like a waterspout its movement can be somewhat erratic and it is not always easy to forecast, although there are certain areas of the world in which hurricanes or their Pacific equivalent, the typhoon, occur and then usually at certain times of the year, so at least you know when you should be on the lookout for them. The enormous amount of damage that hurricanes can cause when they hit land means that now they tend to be identified at a very early stage of their

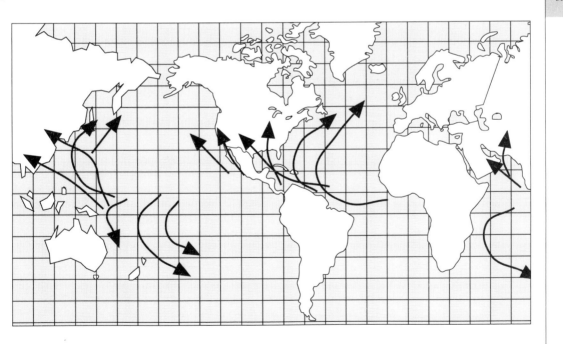

The normal tracks of hurricanes, typhoons and cyclones around the world.

Long streaks of foam are typical of very strong wind conditions where the waves have not had time to build up to match the wind.

development. Their movement is tracked hour by hour so that there should be early warning of their arrival – although predicting the track of a hurricane is an art rather than a science and predictions are not to be relied upon completely.

In the North Atlantic ocean it is the West Indies, the Gulf of Mexico, the Caribbean and the Florida coast which are most prone to hurricanes. In the North Indian ocean it is the Arabian Sea and the Bay of Bengal which are mainly affected and here they are called cyclones. On the western side of the North Pacific they are typhoons and occur in the China Sea, in the Philippine Archipelago, and off the coast of Japan. On the eastern side of the Pacific they occur off the coast of central America and southern California. In the South Pacific they occur off the Queensland coast of Australia and here they are called hurricanes, whilst in the South Indian ocean they occur both on the western side in the region of Madagascar and on the eastern side off the north west coast of

Australia. The seasonal nature of these tropical revolving storms is emphasised by the fact that the greatest frequency occurs towards the end of the hot season in each hemisphere. In the China Sea and northern Pacific, while cyclones occur throughout the year, the greatest frequency is in September as is the case with the hurricanes in the West Indies. In the southern hemisphere hurricanes tend to be most frequent in the January to March period.

Hurricanes
These tropical revolving storms and the normal run of depressions found in temperate climates are essentially similar, for they are both areas of low pressure. The wind circulation is the same, running in a counter clockwise direction in the northern hemisphere and clockwise in the southern hemisphere. The main difference between the two is the strength of the wind, with hurricanes generally having winds in excess of 100mph, whilst the depression will generally have winds of little more than gale force. This is a result of the different pressure gradients within the different systems, and this in turn is usually because of the much smaller area occupied by a hurricane compared with the average depression which can be ten times as large. The actual barometer readings between a depression and the tropical revolving storm may not necessarily be significantly different. A tropical revolving storm can have a very low pressure at its centre, but this is not always the case. A significant difference between the two areas of low pressure is the absence of frontal systems within a tropical revolving storm, whereas these are an essential part of a depression; and this reflects the different ways in which the two weather features are generated. Tropical revolving storms can move up into higher latitudes as often happens in the Atlantic, but when this does happen they tend to lose some of their intensity and they also take on many of the characteristics of a depression, although again the absence of the frontal systems within the circulation tends to make them readily identifiable on weather charts.

Tropical revolving storms tend to form in remote sea areas away from land, sea areas where there tends to be a recognisable area of low pressure but without particularly strong winds. There is usually evidence of thermal activity with the characteristic cumulonimbus clouds and rain showers. These areas tend to be around 10 degrees to the north or the south of the equator but never on the equator because the Coriolis force is an essential part of the development of the tropical revolving storm. Heat and moist air are also essential ingredients, and it is the very moist air and the consequent condensing of the water vapour in this air which provides much of the energy both to initiate the tropical revolving storm and to maintain its impetus. Evidence of this need for moisture comes from the fact that once the tropical revolving storm moves over land it tends to lose strength although it can pick it up again if it moves back out over the sea.

The mechanics of the formation of a tropical revolving storm are less important than its effects. It is satellite pictures which allow these storms to be detected in their early stages and which have done a great deal to remove much of the myth and fear associated with such storms. In a mature hurricane the effects can be found up to 300 miles from the centre – from this outward limit the winds gradually increase towards the middle with gale force winds reaching out perhaps 125 miles from the centre and hurricane force winds extending perhaps 75 miles. A characteristic of the hurricane is the eye at the centre, where the dense and violent cloud suddenly stops to leave a clear area in which the wind can drop to ten or fifteen knots. All tropical revolving storms have very heavy rain, often with thunder and lightning. This rain tends to occur in spiral bands in the outer section of the storm and as the centre is approached the rain becomes more intense and more widespread, reaching its maximum intensity at the wall of the eye. This is why the sudden transition from this very heavy rain and violent winds into the comparative calm of the eye provides a transient relief. Visibility can be extremely poor in a hurricane, partly because of the heavy rain and partly because the sea and the sky tend to merge into one under the influence of the violent winds. Visibility can be reduced down to one or two boat lengths in these conditions and the violent seas also reduce visibility.

One of the main dangers of a tropical revolving storm, particularly as far as small craft are concerned, is that the wind is blowing from opposite directions in opposite semi-circles of the hurricane, and it is this reversal of wind direction which generates some of the extreme sea conditions associated with hurricanes, creating very violent clapotic-type seas which can easily overwhelm small craft.

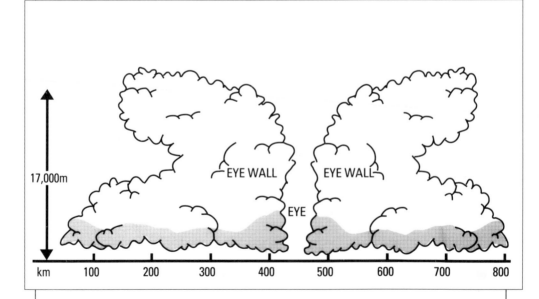

Cross section of a typical hurricane showing the cloud pattern and the eye of the storm. The shaded area shows where rain can be expected, increasing in intensity towards the eye. The horizontal distance can vary considerably from hurricane to hurricane.

Hurricane Approaching

Warnings broadcast by radio are intended to give early warning of hurricanes and should be available in time to allow evasive action to be taken. However without radio there are advance warning signs which will indicate the approach of tropical revolving storms. Like all weather information, this type of local observation is essential even when a radio warning has been received, just in case the storm has deviated from its forecast path.

One of the earliest warnings of an approaching storm is likely to be a swell coming from the direction of the storm. Swell waves are always created by major storms and as they travel faster than the storm itself they can give early warning. Not all approaching swells will herald a tropical revolving storm but any large swell in otherwise good conditions in the sea areas mentioned above should be taken as a warning. Another early indication of an approaching storm is extremely clear visibility and a feeling of oppressiveness in the atmosphere. The clouds can also give early warning just as they can with an approaching warm front and again it is the high cirrus clouds which will give the first indication, and these clouds may well have dramatic colouring if they occur at sunset or sunrise. Gradually the clouds will get thicker, very much in the manner of an approaching warm front. The barometer will not give very much warning of an approaching storm unless you have one which is fully corrected to the point where it is possible to detect small variations in the barometric pressure for the particular time of year. Having barometers of this accuracy on a small boat is unlikely, but still keep an eye on yours because any fall on the barometer in conjunction with the other signs probably means trouble. Bear in mind that tropical revolving storms only tend to

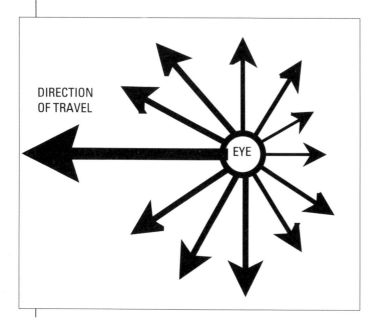

DIRECTION OF TRAVEL

EYE

One of the best early warnings of an approaching hurricane is the increasing swell. This diagram shows the relative size of the swell emanating from a hurricane, the length of the arrows relating to the strength. The maximum swell is found ahead of the advancing hurricane.

occur in specific areas at specific times of the year where the weather conditions are generally very stable. In these particular periods and locations any appreciable change in the direction or strength of the wind should put you on your guard.

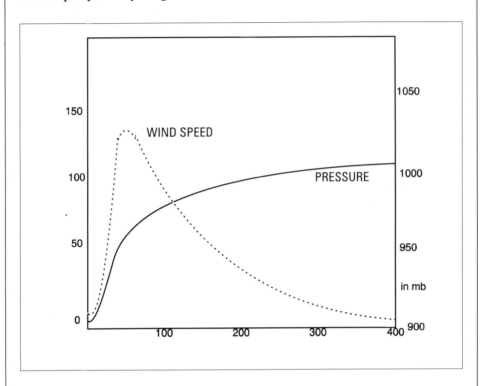

This graph shows how the barometric pressure drops and the wind speed increases towards the centre of the hurricane. There is little appreciable drop in pressure before the wind has increased considerably, so the barometer gives little warning of the approaching storm.

The approximate height of swells in feet which can be expected at varying distances from a storm centre. These are based on knowing the wave height at the storm centre as shown in the first column.

| 0 | Distances in nautical miles --▶ | | | |
	500	1000	2000	3000
40	25	20	12	8
30	19	14	8	5
20	12	8	5	3
15	8	5	3	2
10	2	1	0.5	–

Working Out the Hurricane's Track

Having decided that a tropical revolving storm is approaching, then you need to decide what action to take. For this you need to know the bearing of the centre of the storm and have some idea of its distance from you, the part of the circular pattern of the storm in which your vessel lies, and the probable path of the storm. For the first point you can apply Buys-Ballot's Law which will put the low pressure area on your left when your back is to the wind if you are in the northern hemisphere, and on your right in the southern hemisphere. With hurricanes there is a stronger flow of the wind in towards the centre than there is with the average depression, so whilst the centre will be on your left when your back is to the wind, it will be at more than right angles in the early stages of the storm, probably around 135 degrees. This angle will change as you get nearer the centre and become more directly on your left, but by that time you probably have a good idea of what is going on anyway. Working out the distance to the centre is not easy because a lot depends on the size and intensity of the storm. However the cloud pattern will give you something of a clue and the denser cloud will start probably 200 miles from the centre. Wind speed is another way to judge distance, with Force 8 winds starting about 125 miles from the centre.

From these estimates you can make a rough plot of the location of the centre and from this you should be able to get some idea of the path of the storm. It will be only a rough guide but it may be enough to enable you to set a course to avoid the worst of the storm. Now you have to decide which semi-circle of the storm you lie in. For this purpose the line of progress of the storm is taken as the median line and the right hand semi-circle is the one on the left hand side when you are facing the storm centre, and the left hand semi-circle is on the right. It is the right hand semi-circle which is the more dangerous of the two and where the strongest winds will be found. Here the wind strength is exaggerated by the forward progress of the storm.

If you have any choice in the matter then you want to be in the left hand semi-circle. To help identify which side you are in you need to watch the wind direction very carefully. If the true wind starts to veer, that is go round clockwise, then you can assume that you are in the right hand or dangerous semi-circle. If the wind backs then you are in the left hand semi-circle. If the wind remains steady in direction, then you can assume that you are in the direct path of the storm. The barometer can be a help here in further dividing up the sectors of the storm because if the storm is approaching then the barometer will be falling and if it has passed then the barometer will start rising again.

Escaping from the Hurricane

What you want to do is avoid getting mixed up in the dangerous areas of the storm. In a powerboat with a speed of twenty knots or more you should be able to run away from the storm and keep clear because these tropical revolving storms seldom move at a greater speed than twenty knots. However, bear in mind that the sea may be quite lively at this point in time, which may make progress at this speed difficult. If a powerboat finds itself in the dangerous semi-circle then it should proceed with all possible speed with the wind on the starboard bow which will tend to take it away from the path of the storm. A sailboat should go on the starboard tack keeping close hauled even when the wind is veering.

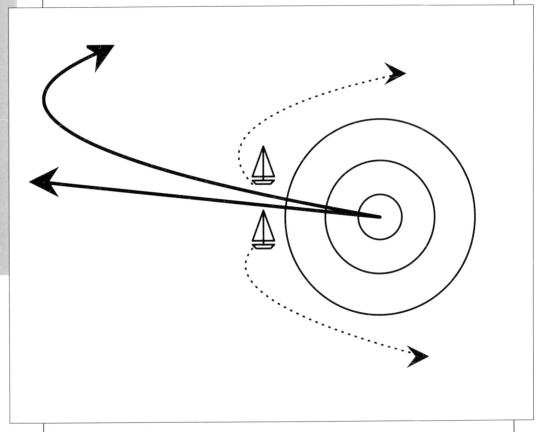

Alternative courses of action to take with an approaching hurricane in the northern hemisphere. The southern alternative is better because it takes you away from the dangerous semi-circle and also away from the danger itself if the hurricane recurves back.

If the wind is backing then you are in what is called the navigable semi-circle and here you should run with the wind on the starboard quarter keeping it in that position as the wind backs. These directions will obviously have to be reversed for a storm in the southern hemisphere.

These avoidance tactics assume that there is plenty of sea room, and one of the biggest dangers with these tropical revolving storms is when sea room is restricted and you cannot follow the chosen course of action.

Obviously you want to avoid the dangerous semi-circle as far as possible, where the sea conditions can become completely untenable, but an even more important priority is keeping away from the land. So much will depend on the individual circumstances, but the diagrams will at least indicate the sort of winds you can expect in the different areas of the storm, and if this diagram can be pictured over your locality with the path of the storm indicated, then at least it will be easier to make the correct strategic decisions to meet the extreme circumstances.

Whilst making assessments of the weather and conditions which presage an approaching storm it is also important to prepare your boat to cope with the extreme conditions. The very strong winds will mean that you can carry either no sail at all or very little, and except in the early stages of the storm it may be difficult to make much progress to windward. The boat will need to be battened down securely and on a sailboat an auxiliary engine could help to maintain steerage way and make a degree of progress. In a powerboat you are in a better position in terms of making headway in a desired direction, but the violent nature of the seas which can be found within the storm could mean that progress is next to impossible, and the best you can achieve is to heave to and maintain steerage way.

There is no doubt at all that tropical revolving storms are best avoided completely and if you sail in areas where these storms are possible, then a vital piece of your safety equipment will be a radio receiver or preferably two, so that you have a back up in case of failure. Whilst it is possible to make an individual forecast of an approaching storm, by the time you are reasonably positive about the signs you could well find that you are too close to take fully effective evasive action. If you know the track of the storm and its speed of progress from storm warnings, then you can plot an avoidance strategy at a comparatively early stage, so that you probably will not experience wind of anything more than Force 8 and perhaps much less. Of course there is the risk that the storm will not follow the prescribed path, but in most cases these storms follow a path which curves to the north in a fairly shallow parabola in the northern hemisphere or to the south in the southern hemisphere. Where you have a choice of avoiding action you should always head away from this probable path.

Tropical revolving storms are one of those phenomena that, with modern technology, seem less alarming, but at best modern technology can only monitor and to a certain extent forecast how these storms are going to behave. You can't hide behind the forecast safely and pretend that the experts know everything that is going on. Of course you should rely quite strongly on what the forecasters say, and they are going to be your best guide, but you mustn't ignore the warning signs of the things which are going on around you. The early indications of trouble can be very subtle, from the growing swell and the high cirrus cloud to the changes in the wind, but all these are the sort of visual signs which you ignore at your peril.

All of the weather phenomena we have discussed in this chapter tend either to lie outside the general weather forecast or to be mentioned in general rather than specific terms. It is only by keeping a careful eye on the changing conditions around you and getting a 'feel' for the weather that you can hope to anticipate some of these short term but often extremely violent weather conditions.

Dangers of Cold Fronts
Apart from tropical revolving storms, a lot of these weather phenomena can be directly associated with the cold fronts of depressions. An active cold front can be an area of quite violent weather conditions, many of which can be quite localised. Thunderstorms, line squalls and waterspouts are examples of intense cold front activity, but sometimes these extremes of weather activity can also occur on a larger scale. Also there may be changes still associated with a cold front, but sufficiently short term to be outside the time scale of weather forecasts. Secondary depressions are a feature of this frontal activity and this is not surprising when you consider that in a very active cold front the change in wind direction can cover a considerable angle, up to perhaps 135 degrees. This very sudden wind shift means that you have two flows of wind moving in almost opposite directions, one warm and one cold, and here you have almost the same set of conditions which initiates the main depressions along the polar front.

Secondary Lows
These two masses of air flowing in different directions have a nearly vertical separation line and it is very easy to picture how this turbulence can generate the swirling mass of a secondary depression. Such a secondary depression can be fed energy from the condensing warm, moist air and here you have the makings of what can be a comparatively local, but nonetheless violent weather pattern. In most cases the forecasters will pick up this developing weather pattern if it has any major significance, but the time scale between the initial development of the feature and its becoming very active can be quite short, perhaps just a matter of hours. The problems occur if the development is just after one forecast period and so no warning is put out until the next one perhaps six hours later. Even that is probably adequate warning for most yachtsmen and may still be within the time scale of a rapidly developing feature, but if you miss the forecast which would have been the one to give you warning of this feature then it may have become a full blown storm and envelop you before you hear the next forecast containing the warning.

The other aspect of these secondary developments is that because they are comparatively sudden in their arrival, you may not have much chance to make an accurate assessment and this could lead you to underestimate of the scale and strength of the secondary depression. They represent an element of uncertainty in the weather patterns, which we like to pretend doesn't exist in this well ordered world, especially since unheralded developments of this type are comparatively rare and so come as an even nastier shock when they do occur. However, it does require a sequence of events for the feature to reach maturity, yet once every so often this sequence of events occurs, perhaps forcing winds up through narrow channels, or funnelling the secondary depression where isobars are compressed over a comparatively small area, so that intense local winds can be created.

Keeping a Weather Log
This emphasises the need for local observation at all times, and this should be more than just a question of tapping the barometer and seeing whether it is rising or falling, and looking at the clouds, or sensing the wind and thinking you will remember what it was like in 4 hours' time to make a comparison. Keeping a weather log should be considered just as vital as keeping a navigation log because when things go wrong and you don't like what you see in the weather up ahead, then it is reference to this log which could give you the clue to what is happening and what may be on its way. You mustn't ignore the weather charts either because these are a complementary source of information, and it is from the weather chart that you should be able to detect the presence of a very active cold front which may be the source of extremes of weather.

Anything on the weather map which looks different from the normal smooth flow of isobars and frontal systems should be viewed with suspicion. The air should be able to flow in tidy, smooth patterns which give a predictable air flow and help to reduce turbulence both on a large and small scale. When you see sharp changes in the direction of isobars or tightly packed isobars, then you can expect turbulence and more extreme weather conditions. In temperate climates these can be looked for as signs of the extremes, but in tropical waters there are less obvious signs from the weather maps because the weather is generally much more settled and the extremes of weather appear more randomly or 'out of the blue' as we say. All the more reason, then, for making regular observations and keeping a weather log, having constantly updated weather charts and forecasts, and being satisfied in your own mind that you understand what lies behind every slight change in the weather that you hear about or observe.

10 Weather Tactics

The forecasts and weather charts are fundamental to your efforts to predict what the weather is going to be; your own observations of what is going on around you will refine that information and fill many of the gaps, and you can make your own assessment of any local variations. This should all add up to giving you a fairly full picture of the weather around you, and in the marine environment there is little excuse for not knowing what the weather is going to do, both in the long and the short term. However it's one thing to know what the weather is going to do, but it is another using this information to maximum advantage to improve the comfort and safety of a planned voyage.

There are some conditions where the decisions are made for you. If it is blowing a gale of wind or the visibility is close to zero, then there will be little or no room for negotiation. In yachting you tend to go to sea for pleasure and whilst some may find a degree of pleasure in battling with the elements, it is important to consider the risks in such an approach. You may get caught out in a gale of wind when you are at sea, particularly on a long passage, but few yachts will be tempted to put out from shelter and take on a gale when they have a choice in the matter.

The problem is that not only are you going to feel very exposed and vulnerable if you go to sea in such conditions, but you will also come under the scrutiny of the authorities. In some countries the authorities may have the power physically to stop you taking what might, at face value, seem to be unnecessary risks, but there are situations where going to sea in such conditions could be justified if you are fully informed about them and any impending changes.

Whilst the wind itself can present dangers, particularly to a sailboat, it tends to be the sea conditions which present the real risk. Putting to sea in gale force winds may not necessarily take you into dangerous sea conditions immediately, and by careful timing it could put you into a position where you can take maximum advantage of a forecast temporary lull in the weather. Such a lull may not last long but it could conceivably give a chance to complete a passage, particularly when bad weather has been experienced for some time.

What this Chapter is *Not* Saying

Let's be very clear about what is being proposed here. Whilst the aim of this chapter is to give you some idea how you can use weather information to maximum advantage, it is certainly not the idea to take the decision making out of your hands. Various courses of action may be proposed, but these are offered as options and you have to remember that one of your options is to stay in harbour. The responsibility for making decisions has to stay firmly in your hands, and safety both in terms of weather and operations must remain with the skipper of the boat. The weather forecaster may get his sums wrong and the weather may differ from the forecasts, but you can't hide behind the forecaster: the responsibility is yours.

Another thing to remember is that you can't change the weather. It may sound obvious, but the weather is there and it will develop and change according to its own laws and there is nothing you can do about that. What you can do is change, to a certain extent, the effects of the weather. In general this will mean finding calmer seas when forecasts suggest it will be rough, getting better visibility or knowing when the visibility might improve, and avoiding rain or local disturbances. By a careful study of the forecast weather and combining this with local observations and a knowledge of the geography of the region you may be able to find areas where you can negotiate with the weather, perhaps by finding improved conditions where there is shelter from the wind or where the sea conditions are moderate even though the wind is strong. You could even reduce the time you are exposed to bad conditions by negotiation. You will always be negotiating with the weather from a position of weakness, but don't let that put you off. Knowing, understanding and exploiting the environment in which you are operating can be part of the enjoyment of yachting.

What You *Can* Do

Bearing in mind that you cannot change the weather, what are the options open to you in your delicate negotiations with the weather? What do you have on your side? Firstly you can alter course or speed, so that you are in a different position relative to the weather pattern. Using this technique you could perhaps run away from approaching bad weather or alternatively get though a bad spell more quickly. Secondly you can stay under the lee of the land or shoals and so reduce the fetch which in turn will reduce the size of the waves. Thirdly, you can seek out areas where the tides or currents are slack to reduce the gradient of waves. Fourthly, you can look for warmer waters or other conditions which could reduce the chance of fog, and fifthly you can use course changes to bring the wind and sea at a different angle relative to the boat's heading to improve the ride and comfort.

These are some of the options which are open to you and you can use them independently or in combination. Using some of these techniques can make quite a surprising difference to the effects of the weather.

Timing can also be an important factor in your negotiations with the weather, where you have a degree of choice. With time available you can wait for a front to pass before going off to sea or you can time a departure to anticipate a wind change which will keep you in sheltered waters when you get to sea. If you are in harbour already, then the strongest weapon in your armoury is to stay where you are, largely immune from the influence of the weather, and where it can't affect your level of risk or exposure to any significant degree.

Running

Let's look at some of these options in more detail because there is a wide variety of ways in which they can be exploited. Speed can be an important factor in negotiating with the weather, and here there is no doubt that the powerboat has the advantage. With frontal systems tending to run at speeds of no more than twenty knots, most modern powerboats have the speed potential to outrun a front. This means that you could outrun the weather to a certain extent, providing of course that the geography of the land allows this. The problem with outrunning the weather in this way is that you can only do so for so long before low fuel or tiredness forces you to give up, but it is an option to consider if you don't like the look of the forecast or the weather is deteriorating to the point where you feel the need to do something about it. This could be a useful tactic to adopt if there is a particularly active cold front approaching and by turning and running away you could be safely in harbour before the front catches up. Such a course of action has the advantage that you will be putting the wind behind you by running away which can allow you to make better speed.

Even a sailboat can delay the onset of deteriorating conditions by running away downwind where progress will be the most rapid, and you could buy valuable time before conditions deteriorate to the point of danger. Running away downwind can have its dangers though, and it is a course of action which needs to be considered quite carefully. Firstly when running downwind, and this applies to both sailing and powerboats, you are not always clearly aware of just how the conditions may be deteriorating. The ride of the boat going downwind will be relatively comfortable because the speed of encounter with the waves is reduced or in the case of a powerboat you might even be overtaking the waves. Progress will be fairly rapid and the ride of the boat fairly relaxed so that it pays to stop and turn into wind every so often to get a better impression of just what the sea conditions are really like, particularly if the conditions are deteriorating. Only then will you be fully aware of the steepness of the wave gradients and possibly breaking crests.

The temptation to run away from the weather downwind can be great, but before taking this apparently easy option, think about what you are likely to find at your destination. With the wind behind you, the fetch of the sea will be increasing with time so that the size of the waves will also be increasing. Any harbour downwind which you think will offer a haven will be exposed to these seas and this means that the entrance to the harbour could be difficult or even dangerous to negotiate, particularly if there is a bar or shallow water at the entrance. If it is an artificial harbour with exposed breakwaters then you could find clapotic seas off the entrance which could increase the risk still further.

Into the Weather
These possibilities emphasise the need to think through any proposed course of action when negotiating with the weather. There is not a lot of point in a short term gain of improved conditions if it leads to a longer term deterioration. An alternative which is open to powerboats, and only to a limited degree to sailboats, is to head upwind into the deteriorating conditions in order to get through them as quickly as possible. This is an option which has to be used only after careful thought, but it does offer the advantage of getting through the worst of the weather and into better conditions as quickly as possible. If you are going to be faced with the bad conditions anyway then such a course of action will reduce the time you are exposed to them.

A situation where such a course could be well justified is where a frontal system is approaching, where you know the wind will veer once the front has passed and the veer of the wind will bring you into more sheltered waters. If you do this with a warm front which can extend over a few hundred miles, then it may be some time before you find the respite you are looking for, and the several hours of heading into rough seas may not appeal. A situation much more likely to justify this course of action would be with a cold front which tends to extend over a much reduced depth so that you could find the wind veering and the sun shining after just a couple of hours or even less of discomfort. With the cold front travelling at twenty knots it could be possible to halve the time you are exposed to it, by heading upwind into it.

Analysing the Forecast
If you are planning to go to sea for the day and the forecast sounds bad it is easy to make a decision not to go. But before you give up, have a careful look at the forecast, and particularly the isobar chart, because you may find that the forecast is talking about a cold front passing through. The forecast will tend to concentrate on the worst of the weather which can be expected, which will be that before or in the front. If you know where the front is located either from the weather chart or from personal observation, then you can think about the better conditions which will normally come along behind the front, and perhaps leave harbour when the front is close or overhead, in anticipation of the better conditions to come. You can put up with discomfort for an hour or two when you know things are going to improve and the head start which you gain could give you the best part of a day of pleasant sailing when the forecast might have

persuaded you to stay in harbour. A sailboat can be limited in taking advantage of this course of action because of its inability to sail into the wind. That would be the quickest way through the front and it could be worth thinking about using the engine to make the transition as quickly as possible. If you do sail through, then sail on whichever tack enables you to take maximum advantage of the anticipated wind veer you can expect as the front passes through. This will depend a great deal on the local geography.

When negotiating with frontal systems there are certain aspects to consider. If you find yourself within 200 miles or so of the centre of the depression then the cold and warm fronts tend to merge into one, and you could have a long time to wait before the better conditions come along. However the change in wind direction will come more quickly, and this can be the important factor if it brings you into a wind-off-the-land situation and the sheltered waters that go with it, so there will be something on your side.

Using Opportunities

Studying the progress of fronts, and the wind and weather changes they can bring, can give you the chance to make a short passage when you have had to shelter from the weather. Imagine a harbour on a south facing coastline where the conditions are exposed in any winds south of west. You are sheltering, but trying to get back to your home port. Watching for that cold front to go through could give you the break you are looking for and if you sail as soon as the rain stops you could take advantage of the break with the wind veering to the north west in what could prove a temporary swing, but one which would give you enough time to make your home port in relatively moderate sea conditions with the wind off the land.

This is the sort of situation you can take advantage of if you have both the weather chart and the forecast available. The change in wind direction may only be temporary and could be limited to just a few hours, and it could be the sort of situation the general forecast could ignore. It may be hard to find evidence of it on the weather map, but the layout of the frontal systems could give you the clues that you need. When you combine these with your own observations, the message of change may become apparent, and what is important is that you are ready to take advantage of it immediately and save a vital hour or two, rather than waiting for the change to be obvious and then finding it disappearing before you can take advantage of it. In such a situation always remember that you still have the option of turning round and going back if the change doesn't take place as you expected.

Timing

This question of timing can have an important bearing on your negotiations with the weather because the weather is in a constant state of flux and change. Good weather and bad weather never last forever and there always seems to be more bad weather than good when you want to make progress at sea. Taking advantage of the periods of moderate or good weather means being ready for them and the yachtsmen who sit in harbour waiting for the good weather to appear before deciding to do anything about it may well find that they have missed the opportunity by the time they get themselves organised and out to sea. This is a situation where the weather forecaster will probably get the blame, whereas in fact it was the yacht skipper who was not ready because he had not anticipated the change in the weather, and so could not take advantage of it. The couple of hours necessary to get the yacht ready and be clear of the harbour could make all the difference between success or failure in taking advantage of a lull in the weather. In your negotiations with the weather, time is often a critical factor and that time can often be measured in hours rather than days. The forecasts tend to be issued on a daily basis and, when you are sailing, you often make your plans on a daily basis, but if you can shorten the time scale down to hours then you will find that it can open up possibilities which will allow you to take advantage of short term variations in the weather.

This is just one example of how pinpointing the timing of change, which we have mentioned in earlier chapters, will put you in a much stronger position when it comes to negotiating with the weather.

Change of Course
Changing course in order to take advantage of weather patterns can open up just as many possibilities as using speed. Most yachts, both power and sail, will experience a rough ride when trying to head into waves and will probably be at their most comfortable running downwind. In many cases the ride characteristics and comfort on board can be greatly improved by an alteration in course of only ten or twenty degrees. Whilst perhaps not strictly speaking negotiating with the weather when you do this, you are certainly negotiating with the waves which are caused by the weather and this is one of the tactics you can adopt in stronger wind conditions to try and make progress close to the desired direction with as much comfort as possible.

Whilst sailboats have no choice when they are forced to tack in order to make progress to windward, powerboats can also adopt the same tactic and can sometimes make faster progress to windward by this tacking technique. In the open sea, tacking in a powerboat is largely a question of finding a more comfortable heading for the boat and making a better speed whilst still making progress to windward. But closer to the coast this same tacking tactic can have a significant effect on the sea conditions and is something worth considering when making a coastal passage. The use of this tactic doesn't have to be restricted to powerboats because sailboats have the option of tacking in either direction when they want to make progress to windward, and the inshore tack can often show significant benefits in terms not only of improved sea conditions, but the wind direction as well.

WEATHER TACTICS

WEATHER TACTICS

Coastwise Strategies

Consider the situation when you have just rounded a headland and want to make a course across the bay to the next headland. There may be a deep, wide bay to cross and whilst the direct course is obviously the shortest route, if this is directly into windward it may not necessarily be the quickest course to follow. From the point of view of a powerboat, if you head into the bay perhaps at an angle of about 45 degrees to the wind, you should be able to make faster progress on this heading in the more exposed sea conditions because you are effectively increasing the wave length and thus reducing the wave gradient which will in turn reduce the vertical motions on the boat. However as you get further into the bay the fetch of the wind will decrease quite dramatically with a consequent decrease in the wave height and this in turn will allow you to make faster speed, so that by the time you tuck in under the land you will be up to full speed. From here you can follow the coast under the shelter of the land, right round to the next headland. By making an incursion into the bay in this way you might increase the distance by half as much again as the direct route across, but the extra speed and comfort can more than justify this and in a reasonably fast powerboat you will almost certainly get to the next headland in quicker time than if you took the direct route across a bay straight into a head sea.

A sailboat can adopt much the same course when there is a choice of which direction to tack. By tacking inshore into the bay you will get into

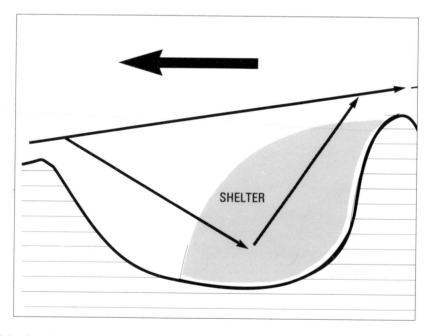

SHELTER

It is often faster, and it is certainly more comfortable, to deviate into a bay to get protection from wind and sea. A sailboat would have to tack anyway, but a powerboat can often make a quicker passage by taking the longer inshore route.

the calmer conditions inshore which will allow better progress to be made and you should enjoy some smooth and comfortable sailing as you tack out to round the next headland. There is always the risk that you will lose some of the wind strength when you get inshore and there is the possibility that you could get headed by the wind where it tends to curl round the headland and follow the line of the coastline. Because of this it may pay you to tack out towards the next headland with a good margin of clearance from the headland in order to avoid these local effects.

Another advantage of tacking into bays in this way, whether it is with a sail- or powerboat, is that it takes you out of the main stream of the tidal flow. When you are heading into the wind, if the tide is with you and beneficial in terms of making progress then you will be in a wind-against-tide situation which will increase the gradient of the waves and tend to make life very uncomfortable, with slow progress. The seas will be reduced if the wind is with the tide, but then the tide will be against you and progress will be slowed even more. The potential advantage gained by the improved sea conditions can often more than justify taking the longer route inshore. Before adopting this tactic you need to be sure that you can round the headlands at each end of the bay in safety fairly close to, and that there aren't nasty tide races off the headlands which you may have to go some way out to sea to avoid. We have already mentioned in earlier chapters the possibility of a relatively quiet passage inside a headland even when the tide race outside can be quite untenable, and this is something

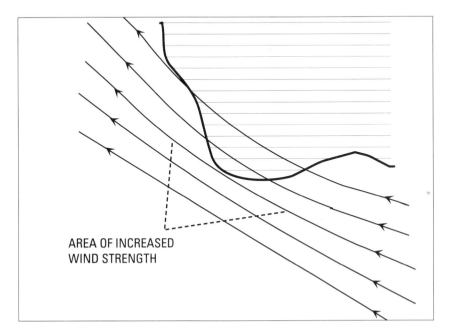

AREA OF INCREASED
WIND STRENGTH

Wind sweeping past a headland tends to contour round the end of the headland even when the land is low lying. This tends to compress the wind making it stronger round the headland.

to bear in mind when formulating your tactics for a coastal passage. If there is a series of headlands like this with strong tidal races off the end, then your only real alternative is to keep well out to sea.

Headlands represent an area where weather, tide and current features tend to concentrate. It is here that wind and water tend to get compressed into a narrower space with a consequent upset in their steady flow patterns. On any coastal passage the headlands represent the milestones, the places where you can expect the worst conditions and where you need to negotiate carefully. If there is adequate water close inshore, then taking the inshore route can offer good possibilities. However, to adopt this course you do need a sound, reliable boat and it is not necessarily a course which might be tenable for a sailboat because any failure or inability to make headway could mean that you are swept into the worst of the tidal race with its dangerous sea conditions. So often you have to commit yourself to a course of action before you get to the headland, and it is not always easy to get reliable information about the prevailing conditions. Any wind reports from a coastguard station or lighthouse on the headland are likely to show a higher wind strength than generally exists because of the concentration of the wind around the headland and also because the height of a measuring station could be well above sea level where the wind strength can be considerably stronger. As often happens when you are negotiating with the weather you may have to resign yourself to a period of difficult conditions when negotiating a headland, but with the promise of better conditions ahead once you have rounded the headland and can head up into the next bay.

Pain for Gain

Part of negotiating with the weather is to be prepared to accept patches or areas of worse conditions when there is a promise of better conditions to come. We have already looked at this when talking about the possibility of going through a cold front to get to the better conditions on the other side. The same applies to rounding a headland when you may have to put up with bad conditions to get to improved conditions on the other side of the headland. Most yachtsmen will accept the situation whereby there is an hour or two hours of discomfort, of difficult sea or wind conditions, when they are secure in the knowledge that having got through that area, there will be better conditions to come. What can be depressing is having to face up to long hours of bad conditions with little prospect of respite. That is the situation you can face when moving in the same direction as frontal systems or in the same direction as a depression.

Sheltering

The shelter which you gain from the land can be a vital help in your negotiations with the weather. Strong winds in themselves are not likely to do much harm provided you reef down the sails on a sailboat, and the combination of strong winds and relatively calm seas can produce some exhilarating sailing. It tends to be rough seas which generate the main risk areas when either sailing or powerboating, and certainly they prescribe the level of comfort which you are going to experience. So sailing under the lee of the land and making use of its protective arm can be a very worthwhile tactic. We have already looked at the benefits of sailing into a bay when making a coastal passage, but even on longer, open passages you can adopt a similar tactic and aim to set a course inside the next headland on the basis that you will get shelter from the bad sea conditions earlier than you would if you took a direct course. So much depends on the relative conditions such as the direction of the wind and the geography of the land, but there are often much better possibilities available than the direct and obvious course and it is worth spending time studying the chart and working out some of the options to see if they are worthwhile. You can often have a number of different options available if there are islands lying off the headland and whilst taking these inshore channels may test your navigation skills, they may keep you in sheltered waters for longer, making this a viable option to consider.

Finding the Wind

Powerboats tend to revel in calm conditions but for the sailboat skipper it is often a question of finding wind rather than seeking shelter from it. Even out in the open ocean the wind conditions are rarely uniform and particularly in the trade winds you can get long lanes of cloud which are the indication of vertical circulation of air. These cloud lanes may be anything from one to four miles apart, and if you are looking for wind then you will probably find the best breeze in the gaps between these lanes of cloud rather than immediately underneath the clouds. Even when there is an overcast sky you often find these bands of stronger winds, typically about five miles apart, so tack across the wind until you find one of these stronger bands and you can then take advantage of it. Remember that

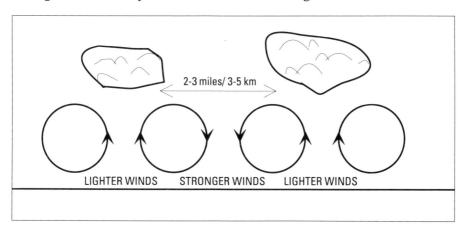

2-3 miles/ 3-5 km

LIGHTER WINDS   STRONGER WINDS   LIGHTER WINDS

The type of local wind circulation which is often found over warmer oceans. The circulation produces 'cloud lanes', the cloud being formed where the warm air rises from the surface.

WEATHER TACTICS

these bands of stronger winds themselves tend to be moving bodily sideways so that once you have found one you want to stay on the starboard tack so that you can take maximum advantage of this area of stronger winds. However if you want to find one of these bands as quickly as possible then you should be sailing on the port tack which will bring you into the fresher breeze at the first opportunity.

Water Temperature and the Wind

Significant changes in water temperature can affect the wind and this is seen to maximum effect in the Gulf Stream where there are significant temperature changes over comparatively small distances. In these areas you may find that the wind speed over the warmer water is double that over the colder water even though there is only a few miles' separation between the two. You could find similar effects to this in estuary waters where warm water is coming off the land and meeting the cold water off the sea, and again you look for the stronger winds over the warmer water. If you sail in the winter or spring, then it is the coastal waters which are likely to be cooler, and the chances are that you will find stronger breezes offshore.

Land and sea breezes are the main daily changes in the wind which can affect coastal waters. They rarely extend more than ten miles offshore and so if you are looking for a breeze in coastal waters then keeping inshore, but not too close inshore, is the best solution, particularly in the afternoon when the sea breeze is likely to be at its maximum. Because of these land and sea breeze effects the lightest winds are often found at dawn and dusk, so that if you are in coastal waters and seeking to make a short passage in a lull in the weather, then dawn and dusk, but particularly dawn, are the periods when you are likely to find the best conditions. It is a recognised feature of weather patterns in many coastal waters that a lull extending for an hour or two can often be found at these times. This lull will tend to be less apparent in stronger winds, but if you need to find a time of reduced winds, this is the time to look for it.

Water Temperature and Fog

Areas of warm and cold water will also have their effect on fog. Trying to negotiate with fog is one of the more difficult tasks you will have to face in coming to terms with the weather at sea. But even here there are a few weapons which you can use. As we have mentioned in the chapter on fog, there are two distinct types and the first thing to do is to find out which type of fog you are dealing with. With radiation fog, it is the sun which will tend to do the negotiating on your behalf and the strength of the sun and its heating effect will determine whether the fog clears or not. It is usually much easier to get *out* of harbour when there is fog than to get back into harbour, and with a radiation fog you are usually quite safe leaving harbour when the fog still persists because you can be reasonably secure in the knowledge that it will be clear when you want to get back into harbour, provided you do this before nightfall. If you actually see the sun starting to shine through the fog this will be an indication that it is doing its work and the fog will clear, so you can be reasonably comfortable in going to sea, particularly if you are heading away from the land where the fog will almost certainly quickly disperse.

With sea fog it is much more a question of the relative temperatures of the land and the air, as this type of fog is usually formed by warm, moist air passing over colder water. You should bear this in mind when trying to determine your tactics, because in the winter it is the water which is closest to the shore which tends to be colder than the water out in the open sea and therefore the incidence of sea fog is likely to be greater inshore than it will be offshore. If you want to attempt to find areas outside the fog then your tactic should be to sail into more open waters but you might have to travel a considerable distance to achieve any notable result. In the summer and the autumn the warmer waters are found inshore where the land tends to help heat the water and so this is where you should start to look when you want to find a clearance in the fog. If the wind is blowing off the land then there is less chance of fog because it will tend to be less warm and moist, and so heading inshore for the lee of the land is the best tactic to try and find a clearance in the fog when sea fog is involved. This tactic can also take you away from the routes of the big ships which can pose a serious hazard to yachts in poor visibility.

The fog which persists on the eastern coast of the United States is a good example of sea fog. This is where the warm, moist air brought in from south westerly winds hits the cold Labrador current coming down from the North, and fog here can be a feature of the weather for nearly fifty per cent of the time in the months of June and July. Here your tactic would be to keep close inshore where the waters are likely to be slightly warmer and the effects of fog likely to be reduced. Otherwise you might have to go a long way offshore before you found any improvement in visibility. In other areas changes in the tidal flow can bring about a change in the temperature of the sea which in turn can reduce the possibility of fog, and if you are stuck out at sea in thick fog then you may be able to pin some hope on the possibility of it thinning or disappearing when the next change in the tide occurs.

Don't Always Seek Shelter

If you are caught out in bad weather, then seeking shelter is one of the things you need to think about seriously. Seeking shelter can be fraught with difficulties because, as we have seen in earlier chapters, getting in under the lee of the land does not always produce the result that you might hope for. Refraction of the waves tends to make them change direction in proximity to the land, particularly around headlands and islands, so that the nice sheltered bay you identified on the chart might prove to be a very uncomfortable anchorage as the waves bend around the headland and enter the bay. To a certain extent the wind will do the same thing, so if you are going to look for shelter in this way then you will probably only find it if you tuck yourself well into the bay, close in under the land when the effects of the refracted wind and waves will be minimised.

When seeking shelter it is important that you bear in mind any possibility of wind changes because the last thing you want is to find yourself exposed at an anchorage. A wind change of 45 degrees can make all the difference between a sheltered and an exposed anchorage and this is the sort of wind change you can expect with the passage of a front, particularly a cold front. This means that even if you are at anchor it is important to keep an eye on what the weather is doing, perhaps even more than when you are at sea, because a sudden change in the wind direction and an increase in wind speed could effectively block the only escape route from the shelter that you thought you were in.

One of the most important aspects when you are seeking shelter is always to consider your escape route. The very nature of any shelter means that you are close in to the land, and there must always be the risk that the wind will change direction and make this land a lee shore. Because of this you need to consider what the wind might do throughout the period when it is forecast to blow strongly, and if there is any risk that it will put you on to a lee shore then you are best to get out of the anchorage at an early stage, even if the wind is still strong, rather than risk being trapped in there and having to beat your way off from the lee shore. In strong winds you are intrinsically much safer in the open sea where you have room to manoeuvre in most directions. You are certainly in a much stronger position to negotiate when you have the luxury of space. Even though it may not be the direction in which you want to go in these conditions, you can at least find the direction which gives you the most comfortable ride, bearing in mind always that when you are doing your negotiating with the weather and your planning and plotting of tactics you must take into account the risk of a failure of engine or rigging which may limit your room to manoeuvre. In a situation like this there is no substitute for sea room and so the temptation to seek shelter and hole up until the wind has gone must be tempered against the risks which could be involved. Seeking shelter is a very valid tactic but you can only undertake it with any degree of security if you have a positive forecast and a reasonable idea of what the wind conditions are likely to be like for at least the next 24 hours.

Weather Routeing
On short passages, up to 24 hours or so duration, you should have good forecasts and weather maps to help you decide your tactics. Even on longer two or three day voyages the weather forecasts should be adequate to plan a route to take maximum advantage of the weather. It is beyond this time that you will have to start thinking about weather routeing. There are two main stages in weather routeing. The first is to look at the statistical weather maps, those showing the general trends and patterns of the weather which can be expected for the time of year. This will enable you to plan the general direction of the voyage in relation to the prevailing winds and expected weather patterns.

Once you have this course laid out on the chart you can then start to fine-tune it for the weather which is forecast for two or three days ahead. To do this you need to have an idea of the performance of your yacht in different wind and sea conditions. For a sailboat there will be a no go area extending on each side of the headwind into which the boat cannot sail. Probably maximum performance on a sailboat will be with the wind on the beam. From this basic information you can lay out lines on the chart showing the expected distance which can be covered on different headings which are close to the required course. From this you can see the optimum course to choose to make best progress and you can repeat the process for each 24 hours ahead for which you have a forecast. The proposed route for each day should take into account the proposed route for the following day to ensure that the route does not bring you into a position where the wind is ahead or where a short term gain might compromise the longer term performance. Whilst weather routeing of this

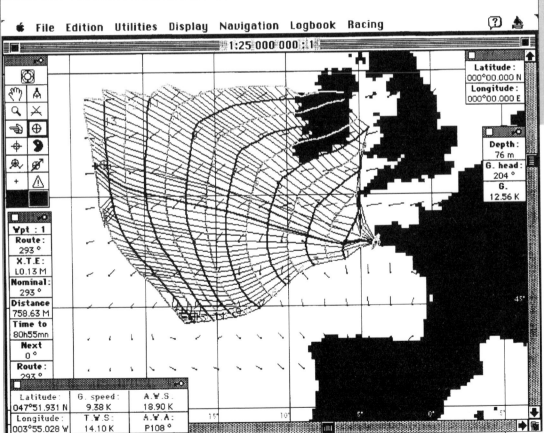

The Macsea computer program incorporates a routeing program where performance of a yacht is combined with weather information to calculate the optimum route to take over a given course.

nature will be primarily concerned with the forecast wind, sea conditions can also have a bearing on progress, particularly for a powerboat.

To undertake weather routeing, and indeed any negotiations with the weather, a great deal will depend on the whole question of weather forecasts and their reliability. If you are going to negotiate with the weather and take maximum advantage of the constantly changing situation, then you want the best possible weather information to do this. If you rely just on the forecast information, which will often be an average for quite a large area and which is unlikely to give any indication of precise timings of changes, your scope for negotiation will be considerably limited. It is almost like trying to navigate without a chart and as far as the weather is concerned, the more knowledge you have, the more experience you have, and the more up to date information you have, the better and stronger the position you are in to negotiate with it.

Negotiating from Strength

We have mentioned the need to look at and consider the weather in four dimensions although most information is presented in just two or three dimensions. The two most commonly ignored are altitude and time. In terms of negotiating with the weather it is time which is the most critical aspect because the forecast itself is generally very good in telling you what is going to happen, but not particularly good in telling you when it is going to happen. If you want to negotiate it is vitally important to know when changes are going to occur.

Throughout this book then, you will find an emphasis on the timing of change and the indications which will allow you to improve the accuracy of your timing of weather changes. If you want to negotiate with the weather with any degree of strength then you must first understand the weather. The weather forecasts and weather charts all give you the basic ingredients of what you need and if you combine this with your interpretation of the information, your assessment of what is going on around you and your appreciation of the various weather features which influence what is going to happen, then your involvement with the weather will put you in a strong position to negotiate. When you can negotiate with the weather, the sea is much less likely to take advantage of you, you maintain a much better degree of control over your constantly changing surroundings, and above all you get a lot more enjoyment and satisfaction from your sailing.

Index

INDEX